ecocide

---AND THOUGHTS
TOWARD SURVIVAL

ecocide

---AND THOUGHTS
TOWARD SURVIVAL

edited by
CLIFTON FADIMAN
and
JEAN WHITE

★ ★ ★ ★ CENTER FOR THE STUDY OF DEMOCRATIC INSTITUTIONS

INTERBOOK, INCORPORATED

Most of the contents of this book grew out of a conference on the threat of ecological crisis which was held at the Center for the Study of Democratic Institutions in 1970. Others were the result of the Center's continuing concern over ecological problems. Some of the material has been published in THE CENTER MAGAZINE. All rights are held by the Fund for the Republic, Inc., P.O. Box 4068, Santa Barbara, Calif. 93103.

Interbook, Incorporated
Box 872, New York 10022

Contents

Introduction

Only a few years ago, as recently as 1966, hardly anybody had heard of ecology; today ecology is one of our most commonly used words. Yet what is it? We know it refers to smog and pollution and the population explosion. We know it counsels conservation rather than exploitation; recycling rather than dump-piling our garbage and waste. We know it teaches us to enhance the quality of our environment rather than to continue multiplying the quantity of our gadgets. Beyond this most of us have a very hazy idea about what ecology really is.

The separate branches of ecology have been quite well established for a long time. Plant ecology deals with the cyclical balances between vegetation and the rest of the environment. Marine ecology deals with the life and matter balances within various bodies of water. Each separate natural resource—our forests, our birds, even our swamps—has its own separate group of ecologists working in special institutes devoted to its study.

Beyond this, we know that ecology deals with all the inter-relationships or "transactions," that occur within the environment. But if this is so, how do we get a grasp on any single ecological problem? For this seems to mean that no matter what we seize upon for study, the fruit fly or the soy bean, we can't understand it until we have understood the universe as a whole. There is a sense in which this is true. At least it is true that most serious ecological problems such as pollution of the air from radioactive particles and the threatened extinction of the salmon or the whale, can only be solved on a worldwide basis. But this is not because the resource itself is found throughout the world but rather because the human organizations and technologies that threaten it require worldwide controls. The thing that inexorably forges limitless interconnections between problems—universalizing ecology, so to speak— is man's behavior.

Human technologies and institutions form an intrinsic part of every ecological problem. Hence, the solutions to ecological problems require alterations in the application of human technologies and institutions: the control of radioactive air pollution and the preservation of the ocean fisheries require concerted and cooperative behavior by men and nations. This means that ecology cannot be divorced from politics; not politics in the ward-heeling sense, but politics in the overall human sense. Moreover, ecology places a stern imperative upon politics. It forces politics to acquire a scope of action comparable to the scope of the problem. If nation-states are too restrictive in scope to preserve the world's ocean fisheries then it is obvious that something in addition to or more than the nation-state will be required to resolve the problem. In sum, politics—politics in the larger sense—is an intrinsic part of ecology. In fact, some men who take a classical view of politics—the late Scott Buchanan is a good example—have argued the other way around, namely that ecology is but politics devoted to a special range of environmental problems, approaching their solution through a special group of ecological sciences.

Contemporary ecologists would not completely disagree even though their own immediate concern is with the special methods and sciences that tell us the dimensions of the problems facing us. Ecology must resolve two very difficult problems that politics alone cannot answer: 1) what are the practical limits of an ecological problem, and 2) how can we reveal the crucial interrelationships of an ecological problem? Both problems involve the use of quite sophisticated mathematical methods.

Because both of these problems deal with networks of relationships, we can visualize them in terms of the "communications" or "transactions" that various components of an ecological problem have with each other. The branch of mathematics known as information theory deals with communications networks of this sort and is heavily relied upon by contemporary mathematical ecologists.

Take the problem of defining the limits of a specific network—say the network of relationships involving the depletion of our salmon fisheries. We can visualize this problem as something like that of defining the limits of human organization, for example, a fishing company. If we take all the individual members of the company and trace all their interrelationships with all other persons, it is conceivable that the complete chain of these relationships would lead us, ultimately, to every living person on the globe, and then back again to the group with which we started. An American fisherman knows a Canadian fisherman who knows a Japanese fisherman, who knows a Chinese fisherman, who knows an Indian fisherman, who knows a Turkish fisherman, and so on ultimately back to the original American fisherman again. But there are also clusters of interrelationships that occur most frequently and these can be measured by their frequency, their monetary importance, their functional importance to each other, and so on. This way we get nodules or clusters of density. Based on such concentrated nodules we can describe the fishing company, or any other network, by the boundaries inscribing these nodules of density. Then we can use a branch of mathematics—say topological mathematics, which studies the configurations of closed systems of relationships—to understand the interrelationships within our chosen network. This is one way ecology attempts to define the limits of a problem and describe its specific problems.

Next, in order to find out more about how changes in one component may affect the nature of the entire network, we can program the whole system of relationships on a powerful computer. Even though we do not yet have big enough computers to do this, in theory we know that complex ecological interrelationships can be understood in something like this fashion. So while ecology is intimately connected with politics, and while its solutions ultimately will require political implementation, it nonetheless represents a new challenge to politics. Its scientific aspects require that we create a new kind of politics in which science and politics will be intimately intertwined; a new kind of science-politics. This, of necessity, will require new kinds of policy-forming, or legislative, institutions. We will return to this problem later. For the present, however, let us look more intently at how contemporary ecological problems arise. Again, we shall be considering not only a natural resource but also the way in which it is affected by human technology. How does the extinction of a natural resource occur? We must know this if we are to know how to combat the threat of extinction.

The message of our day is ecocide, the environment being murdered by mankind. Each day brings to light a new ecological crisis. Our dense, amber air is a noxious emphysema agent; farming—antihusbandry—turns fertile soil into a poisoned wasteland; rivers are sewers, lakes cesspools, and our oceans are dying.

The early warning signals seemed unrelated and were easily ignored. Five hundred Londoners died of a summer smog attack. New York, blacked out and turned off, became dysfunctional. Union Oil's Platform A sprang a leak and converted Santa Barbara's postcard beaches into a sludge swamp. Traffic congestion made driving slower than walking. Airways threatened to become as dangerous as freeways. Cities, unable to function, closed schools and reduced public services. As power blackouts became seasonal, power demands rose and pushed pollution levels—thermal and hydrocarbon—to higher readings. Mathematical ecologists, such as Kenneth Watt, estimate that the United States is approaching the point where the interstitial energy required to keep the system going is greater than the energy it employs productively: Overhead costs overwhelm output. Our entire social order faces an ecosystem "depression" that will make 1929 look like a shower at a garden party.

It is imperative to correct one common fallacy—one especially popular among the young. Technology is not the culprit. Admittedly, the misuse of technology is part of the problem, but the essence of the real problem is what Watt calls the ecocidal asymptote. It is to the new politics of ecology what $E = Mc^2$ was to the thermonuclear era.

The ecocidal asymptote runs as follows: Statistical studies of the pattern of exploitation of every natural resource can be plotted as two curves. One represents the rate of depletion of a resource, the other represents the technological capacity for its exploitation. Both curves are exponential; that is, in the beginning they rise very gradually. But their rate of increase is always rising, pushing their curves up ever more steeply until they reach a vertical explosion. Both follow the same pattern at the same rate, exploding, asymptotically, at the same time.

As an illustration, consider the ocean's fisheries—the blue whale, the salmon, the tuna. In the beginning, the supply is virtually unlimited, and harvesting techniques make little or no dent in the available supply. Soon fishing techniques improve, and, as they do, they gradually overtake reproduction rates; supplies decline as techniques improve. As this situation becomes apparent, it spurs on competition to get more and more while the getting is good. Ever more efficient fishing techniques are invented, and their rate of efficiency rises in direct ratio to the depletion of the resource until the point arrives when the ultimate in fishing technology coincides with the extinction of the species. This "falling together" of the technology and resource depletion curves is the ecocidal asymptote. It is the inimical process that characterizes our age, the enemy of the new politics of ecology. The death of one resource leads to the depletion of another; one technological fix begets another. Each of our ecocidal crises is interconnected with all the others, and none can be solved in isolation.

Harvey Wheeler

Center for the Study of Democratic Institutions
Santa Barbara, California.

1

The Environmental Crisis

In the first part, leading scholars analyze the major aspects of the present environmental crisis. Harvey Wheeler opens this section by describing the symptomatology of ecocatastrophe and discussing environmental economics, thereby deriving several principals of "ecological logic." The ecological problems of the near future, he suggests, cannot be answered by our system of politics—one based on an underlying rationale that this pluralistic, territorially based expression of interests will necessarily produce the general interest. Professors Paul Ehrlich and John Holdren emphasize the strains our continuously burgeoning world population are imposing on the biosphere, our delicate finite system of air, water and other resources. They also examine the psychological effects, particularly in relation to our technologically oriented culture. Professors William Murdoch and Joseph Connell describe the work of the ecologist, but are more interested in conveying the ecologist's way of viewing the world. Survival demands nothing less than its adoption by us all, they argue. Supreme Court Justice William Douglas takes the various federal agencies and then the Congress and the President to task for their negligence in environmental matters. They were all brought into being long before the importance of environmental concerns became evident, and are now unable to take the leadership which is necessary if we are to rescue and restore even our country alone. Doctors John Gofman and Arthur Tamplin, by concentrating on the Atomic Energy Commission and the issue of atomic radiation, provide a stark picture of official bureaucratic behavior in general. The arrogance and unquestioning faith of the scientists, technologists and bureaucrats has continued, with modest adjustments, after each successive revelation of dangers to humans from atomic radiation. Altogether, it is a dismal, seemingly hopeless scene.

CHAPTER 1

Ecocatastrophe

Harvey Wheeler

> *Creature comforts will have to give way to culture com-
> forts. Americans today are at 1788. Never again will
> they or their children enjoy as many material conven-
> iences. This is the real revolution implicit in the new
> politics of ecology.*

Several of the ecological commentators assembled in this book warn us
of an approaching "ecocatastrophe." Of course, ecologists, as a breed,
are as unpredictable as economists, or stock brokers; for every Cas-
sandra there is a Pangloss. But it is extremely difficult to be complacent
when purity, which was once synonymous with "the natural," now con-
notes something artificial: water that is distilled; air that is screened
through electrostatic filters. Let us see what happens if we take the
alarmists at their word: population will grow at such rapid rates that the
world will become dotted with cities of fifty million or more; the individual quest for affluence so eloquently celebrated by classical economics,
is good for us only so long as it is unachieved. The moment it arrives it
proceeds to destroy its host—the assortment of natural resources—on
which it feeds. Technology is to society as heroin is to man: The quest
for an ever more satisfying technological fix is a habit forming drug that
ultimately ravages the body politic. These three—Clifton Fadiman has
dubbed increased population, affluence and technology the unholy trinity of our times—share one thing in common, they have unquenchable
appetites which grow from what they feed on. They create insatiable
demands that force one resource after another into extinction. We have
created a social system dedicated to pandering to their whims—at the
cost of converting the entire environment into a refuse heap. We have so
polluted air and water and so enfeebled our natural resources that biologists seriously proclaim man as we know him will soon be as obsolete as
the dodo. Human survival, whatever that means, will require a new

mutation in man: a new, pollution-resistant and refuse-consuming, breed of man able to conquer and succeed to the more fragile creature—you and me—alive today. All of this contributes to a dread sense of foreboding, a presentiment of ecocatastrophe. But when it comes right down to it, what *is* an ecocatastrophe? If we are all going to die of this modern-age plague, at least we ought to try to find out what it is and how it all came about, before we choke to death in our own offal.

The first question is, how can we describe the symptomatology of an ecocatastrophe? Suppose we begin by looking at an historical example, in search of some general principles. Actually, ecology's first example is *pre*-historical, in the Pleistocene age. But why go so far back into pre-history when ecology deals with the here and now? Ecologists tell us that the main reason is that this is where the best evidence lies. Take, for example, the ecological record familiar to us all, that revealed by the annual growth rings of old trees—not only the old trees still alive, but also the fossil remains of trees that lived hundreds of eons ago in a time that can be located through carbon 14 dating techniques. Such trees tell us a great deal about ecological history: how many rainy and dry seasons occurred, when there were severe winters, and more important, when serious alterations occurred in the seasonal cycle.

Even more exotic, however, is the evidence to be gathered by plumbing down below the surface of our oldest lakes. These, like old trees, are invaluable ecological records. A lake that has existed for 20,000 years or more may in fact be a nearly ideal ecological library. For if its bottom has not experienced too many grave seismic upheavals then during each season of its entire history, airborne particles such as dust, plant pollen, seeds and the like, will have fallen on its surface and settled down to the bottom in successive strata. Careful, deep-drilled core samples can then pull up a chronological history of the overall ecological conditions that have existed from the present on back through the dim eons of the past. We can then correlate this with other findings, and on the basis of our general ecological knowledge, derive hypotheses about the events that must have produced these various aberrations.

One dramatic example of this comes from the ancient lakes of meso (Central) America. Their strata tell us that the level of agriculture existing 10,000 years ago in the western hemisphere was roughly comparable to that which existed at the same time in Asia: the invention of agriculture was not an Asian monopoly. But these lakes also tell us something even more important. For we know that at about that time (10,000 or so years ago) certain events or practices in Mesopotamia led to the increased production of animal life and this, somewhat later, permitted the domestication of goats, cattle, horses and other animals. The result was enormously increased productivity, shortly issuing in the creation of the first high civilizations. In meso-America, however, the opposite occurred. Certain events there led to the depletion, and even extinction, of animal forms that, had they been preserved and cultivated, could have provided the west with an increase in productivity similar to that achieved by the Asians. Civilization could have arisen in meso-America as well as in Mesopotamia. We don't know why these differences occurred. However, speaking as ecologists, we can say that, comparing the East with the West, an ecocatastrophe occurred in the west. That is, had the west perceived the long range potentials of animal domestication it could have instituted animal conservation and domestication practices that could have enhanced the quality of life—perhaps also preventing the later appearance of cannibalism. In short, the prehistoric records of meso-America indicate that about 10,000 years ago there occurred what we would now call an ecocatastrophe.

How do we describe this ecocatastrophe? It begins innocuously. There is agriculture. There is a slight amount of fauna—animals. The animals, being relatively rare, are scarce—a marginal commodity. They are good to eat. There are no totems or tabus to prevent this. The animals are consumed and that is that. The potentiality of domesticating animals is lost for meso-America.

In Asia things proceed differently. Animals may have been no more plentiful in the beginning. Perhaps, however, instead of becoming fair game as a source of food they were revered and their extinction prevented. For whatever reason, however, in Mesopotamia animals were preserved and cultivated and ultimately became available for domestication as beasts of burden. This provided the basis for an immensely heightened level of productivity, permitting the creation of mankind's first civilization.

How do we summarize this? One way is to say that at some point during the Pleistocene era the continued supply of a marginal resource (animals) became of critical importance. A very small variation in mankind's behavioral response to this critical resource would have a massive effect on the future. To decide to eat animals into extinction could mean locking in human culture at primitive agricultural levels. To decide to preserve and cultivate them could make civilization possible. In fact, civilization might never have appeared anywhere had the Mesopotamians followed the same ecological policy toward animals as did the meso-Americans. Clearly, the right ecological policy regarding a marginal resource can have massive consequences. If we judge the situation in the light of what happened we can conclude that the meso-American choice led to an ecocatastrophe, for if the Mesopotamians had later decided on the same policy, their civilization would have been destroyed. That is, an ecocatastrophe is induced when a relatively small behavioral change directed toward a relatively scarce (marginal) resource may result in enormously magnified ecological consequences.

Because an ecocatastrophe is a massive event, our first intuitive surmise about it is that its advent ought to be easy to detect. But our historical evidence indicates that the opposite is the case. The animals of meso-America were like the ocean fisheries of the modern world. Both suffered from the operation of the ecocidal asymptote earlier described. Ecocatastrophe is the massively magnified effect of relatively insignificant changes in the utilization of marginal resources. This is why the onset of an ecocatastrophe is so insidious and also so difficult to detect.

The conclusion is that when something crucial to the survival of a culture becomes marginal, then any ecocidal approach to it threatens the culture, and this is what we mean by ecocatastrophe. But still modern man need not worry. He has technology. He can turn it to new uses and ward off catastrophes, can he not? But what happens then? Here a special problem enters that distinguishes the contemporary ecotastrophe: a catastrophe that threatens not only an individual culture, but the environment, the biosphere, as a whole.

The Environment as a Scarce Resource

Economists often herald the 1970's as the development decade. By this they mean that many countries in the Third World will break out of their traditional economic stagnation through increased productivity. Economists refer to this as passing through the take-off stage. This means achieving very high surpluses that can then be invested in new capital equipment, such as factories and highways. These in turn will bring even higher surpluses, permitting more new capital equipment, and so on into an ever expanding cycle of development. This is the problem of achieving under modern conditions the same kind of productivity increases that first made civilization possible in Mesopotamia eons ago. Economics, the science of productivity, describes the ways in which we can get more out of what resources we use, and also, how to increase the quantity of resources we use: that is, to increase both the productivity of labor and the exploitation of resources. An accelerated rate in the depletion of resources is the price man pays for civilization.

Of course, the second law of thermodynamics tells us that in the end all usable energy will disappear anyway, issuing in the heat death of the Universe. So considering the long run, all civilized man is doing is speeding up the process of entropy. In fact, because all life represents a pattern-formation process that consumes energy, biologists often describe life in general as representing negative entropy. Civilization, with economics as its guide, enormously increases the total amount of life in the environment. Hence, development merely accelerates negative entropy. However, in the higher technological orders, as found today in the industrial West, this process runs rampant. Detroit's automotive industry is the most fashionable example. We have developed a gratification and reward system that leads us to produce more and more autos, without any consideration for function or need, and above all, without regard for the harmful effects on the rest of the environment. The trouble with the auto is that, not only does it represent a direct waste of such resources as iron and oil, it also has secondary side effects that are only revealed much later. By the time we observe these it may already be too late to do anything about them. This is the case with air pollution from automobile exhaust emissions. This is a specifically modern form of the ecocidal asymptote: It works not only directly, exhausting the commodities immediately involved, but also on the environment as a whole. In fact, the environment as a whole may be even more vulnerable than its component parts taken individually. Hence, modern ecology concerns itself not only with the depletion of individual resources, but also with how the overall exploitation system affects the environment as a whole; with what ecologists sometimes call the carrying capacity of the environment. This requires a calculation of how much exploitation the environment can support on a relatively permanent basis, and how much pollution its natural recycling mechanisms can process. For example, taking the United States as an ecological unit, and assuming the maintenance of present levels of technological exploitation, it is clear that something has to change. The environment is being polluted at so alarming a rate that it will soon become uninhabitable. There are only two things that can be done, either cut back our rate of technological exploitation or reduce the population. If we decide to continue present technological levels the United States can probably support only about 150,000,000 people, something like 30% less than our present population. Here we have a new kind of ecocidal asymptote. The elements are, first, the direct rate of resource depletion (the oil and iron we use up); second, the carrying capacity of the environment as a whole (the recycling capacity of our atmosphere), and third, the rate of population increase. The most intractable of these is the carrying capacity of the environment, for any attempt to expand this would almost certainly cause greater pollution side effects than those it sought to eliminate. Consider, for example, the energy requirements involved in building huge air filtration facilities to purify the air over Los Angeles, New York, and so on. From an ecological standpoint it would be much easier, and much saner, to reduce either the level of technological exploitation or the total population level. But either of these would require massive cultural changes: deciding to live in a less intensively industrialized culture, or deciding to take drastic population control measures. However, these "easy" answers seem too repugnant for us to contemplate and we call instead for a technological "fix": some massive technological innovation capable of solving our problem painlessly. Yet this type of technological fixation is the very thing that led to our predicament in the first place. This brings our discussion of ecocatastrophe to a different level.

Originally we defined an ecocatastrophe in terms of the massive effects that might accompany relatively small changes in the utilization of a marginal (scarce) resource. What we find in advanced technological orders is a process whereby virtually all departments of the environment—including the environment itself—become marginal. At such high levels of technological exploitation of resources almost any acceleration in the rate of resource depletion sets in motion an ecocidal asymptote affecting not only the individual resource itself, but also the overall environment as a whole. This is the definition of a culture in mortal jeopardy. It is living at the threshold of disaster. Almost any acceleration it chooses, and acceleration is built into its very nature, forebodes ecocatastrophe.

The Logic of Ecocatastrophe

Let us see if we can now derive some general ecological propositions from the foregoing observations:

1.   First is the notion of marginality; the fact that for any state of cultural development there are certain relatively scarce resources (including institutions and technologies) crucial to the maintenance of that cultural level. Marginality is determined by both scarcity and need. A resource, such as albinos, may be quite scarce, but not marginal. The supply of albinos may be ecologically insignificant in the sense that their total disappearance would have no effect on the viability of the society. In another society, however, distinguished from the first only by the fact that it chooses only albinos for its priesthood, the same condition might make albinos a marginal resource: their extinction would jeopardize the maintenance of a basic institution. Similarly, the supply of a resource such as those with an I.Q. of 120 or over may seem to be overly plentiful in a developing society such as present-day India, and quite marginal in a society such as present-day America.

2.   It follows that societies are dependent upon the continued availability of their marginal resources. But any resource whose supply is marginal may be adversely affected by relatively small changes in its availability. The point at which the rate of depletion makes a marginal resource dangerously scarce represents the threshold point of that society's continued ecological stability.

3.   The maintenance of a given state of ecological stability depends upon the society's ability to maintain the supply of marginal resources at a point higher than their threshold levels of depletion. An ecocatastrophe is the result of any change resulting in the crossing of such thresholds.

4.   While all societies are susceptible to ecocatastrophies, one of the things that characterizes advanced technological societies is that their built-in acceleration of the general rate of depletion tends to convert all

resources, including the overall environment itself, into a marginal resource. The result is that as such societies expand they threaten the entire world with an ecocatastrophe. From an ecological standpoint, the industrial world is intrinsically unstable. Relatively small degrees of acceleration in the depletion rates of any one of a large number of marginal resources threatens the entire biosphere with disaster.

The New Politics of Ecology

The essential ecological problem of the future is, first, to figure out how to preserve general ecological balances, and, second, how to calculate hidden social costs so as to determine how much is really being spent on side effects such as a new freeway, the three-car family, and the SST. Complete ecological harmony is impossible to achieve, but the "trade-offs" necessary to approach it as closely as possible must become known.

There is no such thing as an atmosphere without any pollution. However, it is obvious that certain kinds of air pollution deriving from fossil fuels already have reached perilous levels. This is not merely a question of unsightliness nor even of the threat of a rise in lung cancer and emphysema. Even more serious hazards may develop if pollution particles are carried by superjets from the lower atmosphere into its upper, turbulence-free layers. Scientists warn that these jet contrails may not be dispersed and could act as an insulation layer between Earth and sun, cooling the earth and leading to a new Ice Age. Of course, no one is certain what will really happen. We are in much the same position as when DDT was introduced; nobody knew for certain what its cumulative effects would be. Today, it does not seem inconceivable that pollution particles could quickly clog the upper atmosphere, and before we knew it utter havoc would be upon us.

Obviously, pollution must be reduced, but again we are not dealing in absolutes. We must know what levels are tolerable, and we must know the conveniences or desires that must be sacrificed to maintain these levels. New mass transit systems may be required. Individual desires to own several automobiles will have to be curtailed. And this is but the beginning. Ecologists tell us we shall have to mount a revolution of declining expectations. Gadgets will have to go. Creature comforts will have to give way to culture comforts. Americans today are at 1788. Never again will they or their children enjoy as many material conveniences. This is the real revolution implicit in the new politics of ecology.

What level of public education should we and can we maintain? How much are we willing to pay for it? How can we finance that level? Can we continue to support schools from state land taxes? Is it just to do so? Must we institute a national educational system? To answer these questions we must know the optimum size of an urban community, and how population should be distributed in our clustered communities. In short, we shall have to find out exactly what life in a megalopolis really costs, and whether or not we are getting our money's worth.

What degree of smog is created by population density? Perhaps the same number of people could live in roughly the same area, and even own the same number of cars if they displayed different density patterns with lower ratios of travel between residence and work. Simple freeway tariff schedules could alter traffic patterns immediately by penalizing over-powered and under-occupied vehicles. But we don't know. We don't know how much interstitial overhead energy we waste in a city like New York, merely trying to hold its parts together and keep it operating. We shall have to learn how to calculate the interstitial requirements of cities of different types and sizes to determine the optimum balance between urban amenities and overhead costs. We have no real measures of the price we pay for slums in all sorts of ways—poor health, substandard living conditions, crime, and so on. We do know that slums are high statistics areas; in them are concentrated most of everything bad, and at the end of each statistic lies a dead body.

Automation reduces the number of people required for factory and office operations, making huge cities unnecessary as well as uneconomic. Industrialists have known this for a long time. But what about the city as a cultural center? If we reduced cities to the size of fifty thousand or even a hundred thousand people, wouldn't we have to sacrifice our great cultural centers, our theaters, our museums, our libraries? The answer is no, we would expand them, improve them, and make them more widely available to all. We speak already of the museum without walls, meaning that the treasures of the entire world can now be exhibited everywhere. Microfilm libraries plus computer terminals make it possible for everybody everywhere to use the Library of Congress as well as the British Museum and the Bibliothèque Nationale.

What of the theater, the symphony, the ballet? Of course, recordings and television spread them to all, in one sense. Even great "living" theaters and symphonies are possible in very small cities. Vienna was relatively small when it reached its musical apex. Our greatest cultural traditions have been produced in very small cities. Seventeenth century London abounded with genius; by modern standards it was but a mini-town. Ancient Athens was even smaller, and Plato and Aristotle thought it far too large at that. There is no reason why the same thing cannot be done again. At least, failure would not be due to smallness. All we really need is to decide to produce the cultural conditions necessary to elicit similarly high achievements. Gross size, far from a prerequisite, is an insuperable hindrance.

To answer such questions and to implement the answers will be one of the chief tasks of the politics of the future. We've never asked these questions of politics in the past. But, today, we can have everything that is really valuable about our large cities, and at the same time avoid the disagreeable and expensive side effects due to size. These are ecological questions, and, even though we may be able to answer them soon, there will still be no way to transmit this ecological wisdom to the average citizen for rational and deliberate application at the polls. Yet, this is exactly what we must be able to do in the near future. We shall require a new kind of party system with a new kind of participational democracy seeking solutions to ecological problems. Finally, we shall require a new kind of deliberation or legislative process to grow out of the new politics of ecology, and we shall have to relate to it in something like the way the existing legislative process related to our traditional party system.

Let us take the second problem first, for although it is generally understood that our party system is inadequate the deficiencies of our legislative system have received scant attention. Reflect for a moment on the fact that our legislatures and our party system are well-tailored to each other. Our parties are, as the textbooks say, loose confederations of state and local boss systems. The key element is "state and local." This means that the representatives selected through our present electoral system arrive at our legislative chambers representing the interests of their local districts. An implicit assumption is that all our primary problems and conflicts will arise from the clash of local interests—conflicts relating to the interests people acquire because they live in one place rather than another. Since before James Madison—the man who provided the underlying rationale for this system of politics—we have trusted that this pluralistic, territorially based expression of interests would produce the general interest, almost as if guided by an unseen hand.

But the issues described earlier are not related to any specific territory as such. Nor are they capable of solution through the expression of local interests. On the contrary, the critical problem—the source of our indictment of the old politics—is that its foundation is too restricted and particularistic to cope with the characteristic problems of our times. Technology-related problems know no territorial bounds, and they defy locally based efforts to deal with them. The same is true for science-related issues. Our present political system is unable to bring all such problems together for resolution within an ecological framework. Yet, this is what we must do.

The characteristic political problems of the present arise from disorders of the entire ecological order. Their solutions are to be found, not through the traditional interaction of local interests and pressure-group politics, but through a new politics of the whole—politics considered architectonically, as the ancients called it. This requires a politics that is more speculative and less mechanistic; it requires us to do our lobbying in the realm of thought as well as in the corridors of power. Our most pressing political problems now have their origins in science and technol-

22

ogy. Their solutions will require a new politics especially designed to cope with science and technology, a politics based on what Teilhard de Chardin called the "nöösphere," instead of our accustomed politics based on real estate. It follows that entirely new policy-forming institutions will be needed to deal with the ecological politics of the nöösphere. Legislatures must be redesigned accordingly. But, of course, before all this can happen, the popular base from which representatives are chosen must be given a new foundation. The scientific-biological-technological revolution that awaits us around the corner of post-industrial time demands entirely new ecological parties.

Dr. Harvey Wheeler is a Senior Fellow at the Center for the Study of Democratic Institutions. He came to the Center in 1960 from Washington and Lee University in Lexington, Virginia, where he was Professor of Political Science.

Dr. Wheeler received his A.B. and M.A. degrees from Indiana University and his Ph.D. from Harvard. After serving in military government in the European theater during World War II, he taught political science at Harvard and at Johns Hopkins University.

In addition to monographs on political science and political theory in numerous academic and polemical journals, Harvey Wheeler is the co-author, with the late Eugene Burdick, of the Novel *Fail-Safe*.

In 1968, *Democracy in a Revolutionary Era* was published by *Encyclopedia Britannica* both as a part of their 200th Anniversary *Perspectives* series and in book form (Praeger Inc.). It is a major essay by Dr. Wheeler on contemporary and future political concerns. Also released in 1968 are his contributions to *Alternatives to Violence* (an anthology including Dr. Wheeler's "Moral Equivalent to Riots"), and Nigel Calder's *Unless Peace Comes*, in which Dr. Wheeler discusses "The Strategic Calculators."

CHAPTER 2

An Inventory Of Disaster

Paul R. Ehrlich
John P. Holdren

> *Outside of the standard plans which Stanford has, I*
> *carry no insurance, make no plans for retirement.*
> *Long-range planning just seems silly to me as long as*
> *the world keeps running downhill at the rate it's going*
> *now.*
>
> Paul R. Ehrlich

The Ascendancy of Man

The most startling terrestrial event in the two-billion year history of life on the Earth has been the rise of the species *Homo sapiens* to its present position of global preeminence. A mere ten-thousand years ago mankind was but one of many species of large mammals. He numbered perhaps five million individuals, at that time a far smaller population than that of such species as the bison. But even then, man's skill at hunting and his mastery of fire foreshadowed the colossal threat to the planetary ecology he was to become. There is substantial evidence that Pleistocene man in America caused the extinction of 70% of the land mammals of large size—such as mammoths, horses, and camels. In Africa, man wiped out perhaps 30% of the megafauna. Finally, many ecologists attribute the existence of the world's great grasslands to primitive man's use and misuse of fire.

About 8000 B.C., on the edge of the Fertile Crescent in western Asia, the first groups of men gave up the nomadic life and started to practice agriculture. This change, which marked the inception of a revolution which is still in progress today, was perhaps the most important single happening in the history of the earth. It started a trend toward increased security from hunger for mankind, and initiated an irregular but persistent decline in the death rate in the human population. As the beginning of the systematic modification of the planet for the support of human beings, this change provided the springboard for mankind's dramatic leap to dominance.

The agricultural revolution has been going on now for some ten thousand years; until a few hundred years ago it was the major cause of the decline in the death rate. Because population growth is a function of the difference between the birth rate and the death rate, and since the birth rate over these many centuries has remained relatively high, the spectacular rise of the human population during this period can be attributed directly to the agricultural revolution. It, virtually alone, caused the hundredfold increase from some 5 million people in 8000 B.C. to 500 million in 1650 A.D. And thus it fueled the first long pull in man's unconscious quest to determine by experiment the ultimate carrying capacity of this planet.

Since 1650, the agricultural revolution has been joined in the work of shaping civilization by two further revolutions, industrial and biomedical. And while the fruits of these two newcomers have in large measure been unequally enjoyed, their effects in further reducing the death rate have been almost universal. Hence, while the quality of life has gone up dramatically in some places, the quantity of life has gone up dramatically everywhere. At this writing the human population, at over 3.5 billion, is more than 700 times its size at the start of the agricultural revolution; an increment equal to that "initial" 5-million human beings is now added every 26 days.

The Price of Growth

The achievement of these remarkable figures through the interacting effects of the agricultural, industrial, and biomedical revolutions has entailed not only the profound modification of man's environment but also its piecemeal disintegration. This is not surprising in view of man's historical and persistent reluctance to consider goals and consequences which transcend the immediate or the local. We have occupied ourselves with constructing the ingredients of the revolutions themselves because these ingredients met immediately perceived needs. But we have failed to develop the social machinery to direct and control our expanding manipulative and technological abilities, because the consequences of not doing so have not been obvious. Indeed, it is our ever-growing expertise at building our technology and modifying ourselves and our planet, all in the absence of carefully considered goals, that is at the heart of what is today being called the Biological Revolution.

The consequences of our shortsightedness are now being more widely felt for two reasons. First, improved communications have heightened our awareness of human misery—which has always existed but was once easier to ignore. Second, the sheer weight of our numbers and the unprecedented power of our technology have so overtaxed the buffering capacity of the globe that only the most unperceptive can dispute the rapid deterioration of the environment on every side. Unfortunately, the recognition of the symptoms is even today only rarely accompanied by a grasp of the cause. Thus we are still promised relief by ardent advocates of the same patchwork combination of heedless growth and technological band-aids which has put us where are are today.

It is worth reviewing briefly just where that is. Of the 3.5 billion people packed onto the planet, over half a billion are undernourished (they receive too few calories) and over a billion are malnourished (their diets are deficient in some essential constituent, usually protein). The consequences are especially severe among children—those who escape death by starvation often suffer permanent mental retardation from the lack of high-quality protein. And while it would take an overnight increase of perhaps 30% in world food production to feed today's population decently, that population is growing at a rate which will double its size in only 35 years. The contention of certain well-fed journalists that the "Green Revolution" will keep food production ahead of population growth over the next few decades is patent nonsense—food production has hardly begun to catch up. Hunger is of course only one aspect of the incredibly low standard of living in the "less developed" countries of the world. At last count, the relatively well-off one-third of the world's population accounted for 87½% of the global equivalent of gross national product (GNP). The remaining 2.4 billion people had 12½% of the goods and services to divide among them. Despite intensive international efforts to reduce this politically explosive gap between the "haves" and the "have-nots," the disparity is at this moment still increasing.

Agricultural technology has developed to the point where very high food yields per acre are attained under certain conditions, primarily in the temperate zone. But the grave ecological consequences of this technology are all too often ignored. Furthermore, modern "space-age" fishing technology and the escalation of pollution threaten to deny man access to the resources of the sea, resources on which he depends heavily for the all-important protein component of his diet. These resources are not unlimited, contrary to what one often reads in the popular press. Considering current patterns of utilization we may already have exceeded the annual sustainable yield, and even under utopian conditions more than a fewfold increase would be difficult to obtain.

Moreover, medical scientists in the United States have followed the flow of federal money and put a great deal of effort, with varying degrees of success, into curing the diseases of middle-aged congressmen. Thus we have the spectacle of vast resources poured into programs leading to heart transplants for a very few individuals in a country where many millions are malnourished. The United States is, furthermore, a nation which ranks only fifteenth in the world in infant mortality. It is, on the other hand, fortunate that the serious ethical problems associated with organ transplants and prostheses are being aired now, while they are still a minor sideshow as far as the mass of humanity is concerned.

For in the unlikely event that mankind should solve its pressing problems, reduce the size of the human population, and preserve a world in which medical science flourishes, these questions will become serious beyond anything contemplated today. The most elemental questions will be "What is an individual?" and "How long should an individual's life be preserved?" There is no theoretical barrier (that we can see) standing in the way of eventually achieving individual life spans of hundreds or even thousands of years, even though we have not yet made progress in this direction. (We have increased the average life span, permitting more people to live out what is probably a genetically determined span. But there is no known reason why we should not discover how to extend that span greatly.) And it is abundantly clear that in the near future the problem of rejection of transplanted foreign tissues will be more or less solved, and substantial life extensions by transplants will be possible. But where will the replacements come from, who will pay for them, and who will decide on the allocation of parts in short supply?

The most revolutionary of all of man's prosthetic devices probably is the computer, which may be used as a replacement for, or an extension of, the human mind. Computers, in conjunction with modern communications systems, have already revolutionized the lives of people in the developed countries. They have done much more than facilitate the obvious breakthroughs in science, technology, and social science. Computers have changed the power structures of institutions from universities to governments; and to some degree they have taken decision making out of the hands of human beings. Indeed there is now talk that technological advances in armaments may require such rapid reaction times that computers will have to make war/no-war decisions. The thought is hardly cheering.

Man has begun to turn systematically, for the first time, toward the frontiers of the mind. At a strictly empirical level so-called "brainwashing" has demonstrated the kinds of horrors which are possible. Holistic experiments on the mind, using such diverse tools as drugs, hypnotism and electrical and surgical intervention are being used increasingly to "change minds." Computers also enter the picture here in educational roles. They have, for instance, been used successfully to teach problem children to read and write. Slowly but surely, biologists are beginning to unravel the secrets of the nervous system and are learning the bases of perception and memory. It seems a safe assumption that various kinds of controlled biochemical manipulation could, of course, be for what almost everyone considers an obvious "good," for instance, in the cure of mental illness or retardation. However, the potential for misuse of this power—accidental or intentional—hardly needs elaboration.

From these few examples, we can see that biological revolutions have confronted us with a set of extraordinarily difficult social and political problems; problems which are multiplying and growing at an incredible rate. The root of all these problems is an increasingly efficacious biological technology originating in the technology of agriculture (if man had never practiced agriculture it is unlikely that he would ever have practiced molecular biology). There is a tendency to solve problems created by biological technology by encouraging its further growth, without any careful consideration of the goals or consequences of such growth. Thus we see the further development of ecologically naive agricultural technology as a "solution" to the population-food crisis. How do we solve the problem of too many people? Develop a better contraceptive technology, but neglect critical questions of human attitudes toward reproduction. Shortage of organs for transplant? Grow them in tissue culture or develop artificial organs. Information overload? Build bigger and better computers and communications networks.

The question that most needs asking is all too rarely asked: *What for?* What kind of life are those additional people we feed going to live? What will the composite men of the age of transplants do with their extra years of life? When we can "improve" our minds genetically or biochemically, what kind of world will we have to think about? What kind of information will flow through our improved communications networks and be processed by future generations of computers? Is Western cultural evolution taking us where we want to go (and is it taking the rest of humanity where it wants to go?). These are some of the fundamental questions raised by the biological revolutions of the last eight thousand years; and, as the pace of change accelerates, our chances of satisfactorily answering them and modifying our behavior appropriately are diminishing rapidly. It is possible that the rapid growth of technology will lead to that common end of runaway evolutionary trends—extinction. The signs now point that way, and the time for breaking the trend is short.

The Pursuit of Disaster

It is widely held that the "solution" for these difficulties is to develop the rest of the world after the standard of today's industrial nations. Most observers acknowledge, of course, that so complex a process will be too slow to avert entirely the convulsions of famine and social disintegration whose precursors are already being felt. But all too few have questioned the validity of the development concept itself. We are suggesting here that the overdeveloped West, with all the short-sighted exploitation of the environment and pillage of resources which have attended its "progress," makes a miserable model for anyone to follow. Indeed, in view of the grave threats which the abuse of technology has already posed to the environmental systems on which all life depends, one can argue that to batter the rest of the world into "prosperity" with the same technological bludgeons would be ecological suicide.

This is not to belittle the need for improving the quality of life in most of the world, or even the role that technology must play in the attempt. But it must be made clear that even *one* 300-horsepower automobile per family represents a level of consumption inconsistent with the long-term sustenance of even the present population of this planet; that the elevation of the poor to a nominal degree of affluence must be accompanied by the descent of the rest of us from the excessive affluence we enjoy today; that "quality of life" means breathable air, drinkable water, and the hope of a future for one's children, none of which are measured by GNP; and, finally, that all the technology brought to bear on the considerable problems of mankind must be tempered with an unprecedented concern for the long-term livability of this fragile and finite "Spaceship Earth."

For the lack of such perspective we are today in a precarious position indeed. The remainder of this chapter eleborates the threats to our health, sanity, and survival which overpopulation and our attempts to support it have so sorely aggravated. The subject matter is categorized according to the "level of insult" to man and his environment; direct or subtle, continuous or discrete, catastrophic or merely corrosive. Some of the threats, such as persistent pesticides, appear in more than one category. Others are only vaguely understood, and may ultimately prove to be less (or more) serious than we imply. Nor do we claim that this bleak survey is exhaustive—new threats materialize regularly—but those we cite are reason enough to question the ethic of unending growth which spawns or nurtures all of them.

Continuous Assaults on Man and His Perceived Environment

Air Pollution

Virtually every major metropolis in the world has an air pollution problem, and the rate of expansion of urban complexes everywhere is rapidly making the brown pall and smarting eyes ubiquitous symbols of "progress". Unfortunately, there is more to air pollution than darkened skies and minor discomfort. Human death rates, particularly among the very young, very old, and those with respiratory ailments, are correlated with heavy smog concentrations. To date the few dramatic disasters associated with smog (such as the estimated 4000 fatalities in London in the 1952 episode) are nevertheless overshadowed by the potential long-term health hazard to vastly greater numbers of people.

The amounts of material involved are staggering and the physiological consequences extensive. In the United States alone, automobiles spew 66 million tons of carbon monoxide, 12 million tons of hydrocarbons, 7 million tons of sulfur and nitrogen oxides, and 1 million tons of miscellaneous particulate matter into the atmosphere every year. Steel and paper mills, refineries, chemical plants, power stations, heating, and trash burning add more matter, to a grand total of 140 million tons of filth and assorted poisons annually. Symptoms of acute carbon-monoxide poisoning—headache, nausea, decrease of coordination—are not uncommon in freeway traffic jams, and cases of chronic carbon-monoxide poisoning have been reported. Sulfur dioxide reacts with air-borne droplets to form sulfuric acid and is suspected in increasing rates of acute and chronic asthma, bronchitis, and emphysema. Nitrogen oxides react to form photochemical smog, and, in higher concentrations, cause constriction of the bronchi and tissue damage in the lungs. Various hydrocarbons and some kinds of particulate matter are known or suspected carcinogens; a number of studies have demonstrated a strong correlation between incidence of lung cancer and geographical distribution of air pollutants.

Unfortunately, available data are inadequate for evaluating comprehensively the public health consequences of long-term exposures to low concentrations of common air pollutants. The difficulties arise from uneven and incomplete reporting of both air pollutant levels and public health data, and from the wide variety of environmental factors in addition to air pollution which may be affecting health. The lack of sufficient information to sort out the various effects is occasionally mistaken for "proof" that air pollution at today's typical concentration is no more than a nuisance. Such an attitude is particularly foolish in view of past experiences in such matters, where increasing experience and improved data have so often revealed serious hazards where none were thought to exist.

Animals other than humans are of course also adversely affected by air pollution, as are plants. High levels of pollution can be expected to have immediate effects on plant and animal productivity and even survival. Lower levels do systematic damage which may be longer in showing up, but is eventually devastating. A current example is the demise of some 100,000 acres of pines in the mountains overlooking Los Angeles, which is caused by the trees' unfortunate location at the elevation of that city's infamous inversion layer.

Our limited knowledge of the details of air pollution permits little hope for early relief. The meteorology of air pollutants is in its infancy, and only a few of the chemical reactions which these substances undergo in the atmosphere are well understood. Over 70% of the particulate contaminants in urban air have not even been *identified*. The biological effects of these unknown substances are open to speculation. As their concentrations increase, we shall certainly find out. It is also worth noting that present automotive smog-control devices, while they reduce sulfur oxide and hydrocarbon emmissions, actually increase those of the nitrogen oxides. Panaceas are not easily found. Electric cars, for example, would simply shift part of the pollution burden to the locations where electric power is generated. Some pollutants, such as asbestos particles from brake linings and miscellaneous polymers from tires grinding against pavement, are independent of the source of motive power.

Water Pollution.

Civilized man is by now well aware of the more obvious symptoms of water pollution: scum-covered rivers, stinking bays, and shorelines littered with bloated fish. The cause of much of it is equally clear: the indiscriminate dumping of raw sewage and industrial sludge into the nearest body of water has exceeded the absorptive capacity of the environment. Because the symptoms of this overflow are so compelling, it seems likely that we shall finally attempt to do something about it. But continued population growth makes it improbable that we shall find the funds to do more than skim off the chunks.

Unfortunately, the most serious water-pollution threats are those which cannot be seen, smelled, or picked up by the handful. The organic content in many domestic water supplies which have been treated to some degree is apparently still high enough to protect viruses from the effects of chlorine. Hence tap water is a suspected transmission route for the alarming rise of infectious hepatitis in the United States today. Moreover, the vast array of chemicals which industry spews into the environment in many cases defies filtration. These chemicals now pervade not only rivers, lakes and even oceans, but also vast reservoirs of ground water. As with air pollutants, their possible toxic effects have in most cases not even been adequately catalogued. Many, of course, are *known* to be fatal to fish, the mainstay of high quality protein supplies in much of the world.

Several particularly insidious forms of water pollution result from the extensive use of fertilizers in modern agriculture. These nutrients are carried by irrigation and rainfall runoff into rivers and lakes, which they effectively overfertilize. The result is the rapid growth of certain kinds of algae, which periodically reach incredible abundance in "blooms," then die. The decay of the great masses of algae depletes the supply of oxygen dissolved in the water, leading to massive fish kills. A second and only recently discovered consequence of heavy fertilization is the accumulation of nitrates in local supplies of ground water. Unfortunately, the digestive tracts of farm animals and human infants often contain bacteria which convert the harmless nitrates to highly toxic nitrites. The result is a blood disease, methemoglobinemia, characterized by labored breathing and possible suffocation. Cases have been reported in California and in the Midwest. In view of such problems, the projected ten-fold increase of inorganic fertilizer consumption in the United States in the next thirty years poses a frightening threat.

Pesticides

The harmful effects of persistent pesticides, principally the chlorinated hydrocarbons such as DDT, have only recently attracted public attention. Most of the consequences of their widespread use are quite subtle and slow to be detected; accordingly, these aspects will be discussed in the next section. Two effects which could now be called obvious, however, are the frequent failure of pesticides to achieve one of their stated objectives, namely increased productivity, and the related problem of eradication of useful, non-target species. The difficulty is that the population most resistant to the pesticide is often that of the target pest, and the most susceptible populations are those of the pest's natural enemies. One reason for this is that the population of the pest is larger than those of the creatures which feed upon it, and the probability of a resistant strain developing increases with population size. As a result, broadcast use of nonselective pesticides tends to kill more useful organisms than pests (the farmer is then encouraged to apply larger doses to cope with the population explosion of, say, weevils, whose natural enemies have been eradicated). Available evidence indicates that although use of persistent pesticides has increased many times over in the last twenty years, the *fraction* of food crops lost to pests in the fields has remained relatively constant at about 10%.

It is now well established that certain birds and fishes are already being poisoned as a result of chlorinated hydrocarbons being concentrated as they pass up the biological food chains. Some species of birds, particularly fish-eating hawks, eagles, and sea birds (which eat four or more steps up from the base of food chains), may be threatened with complete extinction. Part of the difficulty is that the pesticides interfere with the birds' calcium metabolism in such a way that the eggshells are too thin and are thus easily crushed. Coho salmon, which also feed high on the food chain, have been passing pesticide residues into their eggs. In 1968, almost 700,000 young Lake Michigan salmon died as they absorbed the last drop of DDT-rich oil from their yolk sacs. And DDT concentrations are now rising ominously in such important food fishes as tuna, mackerel, and hake. The more subtle effects of biological concentration of pesticides will be mentioned later; the birds and fish are cited here because the problem is already quite visible. As will become clear, there is good reason to believe that the birds and fish are only the *first* victims.

Soil Erosion

Soil is not just a collection of crushed rock arranged to keep plants from blowing down in the wind. It is a complicated collection of organisms—bacteria, fungi, protozoa, worms and insects, to name a few—all of which participate in the retention, conversion and processing of the nutrients used by plants. The biological community of fertile topsoil is "produced," as it were, at the rate of about one inch every three-hundred to one-thousand years. The dispersal of the same amount by wind or water, aided by the shortsighted logging, grazing, and cultivation practices of man, may take as little as a day or even an hour. The process of erosion is of course not deterred by the use of fertilizer, nor can the addition of these few inorganic chemicals be expected to compensate for long for the loss of the topsoil itself.

At a time when population growth demands ever-increasing areas of productive land, the record of our essentially permanent losses to erosion is most discouraging. The fraction of the Earth's land surface classified as desert and wasteland has increased from less than 10% to over 25% in the last century. The Sahara, in part a man-made desert, is advancing at several miles per year over a broad front. The Great Thar desert of India, also partly man-made, is advancing at 5 miles per decade around its entire perimeter—its area has increased by 60,000 square miles in ninety years. And it is worth noting that in India, one of the hungriest countries on earth, over half of the existing farmland is inadequately protected against erosion today.

Secondary to the immediate loss of agricultural productivity, but still very costly, is the damage done by the soil once it has been ripped from the land. The burden of silt carried by many of the world's rivers fills irrigation and hydroelectric reservoirs on a time scale of decades for significant loss and a century or so for total destruction. Thus are defeated some of the very measures intended to compensate for the original erosion losses elsewhere. A final casualty of the silt load in rivers is the gravel beds needed by anadromous food fishes, principally salmon, to spawn. The beds not already made inaccessible or unusable by dams are being continuously converted to pebble-bearing muck, carrying yet another species further down the road to extinction.

Thermal Pollution

The combination of growing population and increasing per capita use of energy has led to a phenomenal growth in the power requirements of civilization—world energy consumption is doubling every seventeen years or less, more than twice as fast as population. Herein lies yet another threat to both local and global environments. For according to the laws of thermodynamics, waste heat is the inevitable companion of usable energy – not only is heat a by-product of power generation processes but even the useful power itself is ultimately degraded to heat. The former effect manifests itself as the heat which goes up the stack in a coal-fired electric power station, and in the heat transferred to water used for cooling in both fossil and nuclear-fueled plants; the latter effect is seen in the heat from cities, which in some instances already perceptibly alters the climate in surrounding areas. The problem of disposing of the heat at the consumption end of civilization's energy flow will ultimately be a global one; it is discussed in the section on "subtle assaults" on the environment.

The problem of handling the relatively concentrated heat at the sites where power is generated is upon us today, and is worsening rapidly. It has been aggravated by the fact that nuclear generating plants are thermally less efficient than their fossil-fueled counterparts; that is, they produce more waste heat per kilowatt of electricity. Moreover, nuclear plants become more economical with increasing size, so the trend has been toward larger and larger installations. This increases still further the amount of heat which must be handled at one site.

The numbers involved virtually dictate the use of water, as opposed to air, as the primary coolant, and the amount of water required (1 to 2 cubic feet per second for every megawatt of installed capacity) makes borrowing from a lake, river, or ocean almost a necessity. The water is returned to its source from 12°F. to 25°F. hotter than it started, and herein lies the threat—immediate and potentially catastrophic damage to aquatic animals and plants. Installations on the open coastline will be least harmful because of the enormous volume of cold water available to dilute the heated discharge—but even here local effects on kelp and other inshore biological communities can be anticipated. Outfalls on estuaries, bays, and inland lakes, where dilution is much less effective, will cause drastic changes in marine ecology. By far the worst prospects, however, are those for the world's river systems. It is estimated that by 1985 fully one-quarter of the total annual runoff of the United States will be cooling power plants. Since much of the total actually occurs during a relatively short flood season, the fraction will be closer to half for most of the year. This will mean the virtual extinction of much of the flora and fauna which inhabit our rivers today, including a number of valuable food species. It should be noted that the biggest threat which warm water poses to aquatic life is its reduced content of dissolved oxygen. Because other pollutants already discussed consume water-borne oxygen, we can expect destructive reinforcement of these effects to hasten the demise of freshwater life.

The few alternatives to the use of ocean, lake or river water for cooling power plants are expensive and hence unpopular with utility companies. Open-cycle cooling towers are costly to build and require the purchase of water which is consumed by evaporation. Closed-cycle towers, which use the same water over and over, cost even more to build, and cooling ponds require the acquisition of two acres of increasingly expensive land per megawatt of plant capacity. All of these alternatives spare marine life by pumping the heat into the atmosphere. The consequences are then climatological; some which have already been experienced in Europe are heavy ground fogs and frosts (associated with the water vapor from open-cycle towers).

Utility companies argue, as do polluters of every stripe, that mankind must choose between their indispensable product and some "minor" aspect of an evidently very dispensable environment. They seem unable to grasp that the real choices are not of the form, "energy—take it or leave it," but rather of the nature, "energy—increase the supply hastily (at the expense of the habitat) or moderate the demand (at the expense of population growth and 300-horsepower cars)."

Noise

The spectacle of headlong mechanization and urbanization of growing populations has been accompanied by a veritable cacophony of ever louder and more discordant sounds. Today the problem is most clearly recognized by people unfortunate enough to live in airport landing and takeoff patterns, and those whose teenagers have suffered permanent hearing impairment at rock concerts. And while "noise pollution" is undoubtedly more amenable to solutions employing technology and determination than are most pollution problems, these ingredients are not being applied to the task in the requisite amounts today.

Sound levels are customarily measured in decibels—a logarithmic scale on which a ten-fold increase in the intensity of the noise adds ten decibels. Thus a 100-fold increase in loudness adds 20 decibels, a 1000-fold increase adds 30. On this scale, the threshold of hearing is zero decibels, a typical conversation is 60, heavy traffic or a jet passing overhead is 100, and a jet taking off or a machine gun at close range is 120. Sleep interference can occur as low as 50 to 55 decibels, and there is growing evidence that noise in the 90-decibel range causes irreversible changes in the autonomic nervous system. There are also indications that noise is a factor in such stress-related conditions as peptic ulcer and essential hypertension. And while the data are still spotty, we can rest assured that the "experiment," with most of mankind serving as guinea pigs, will go on.

Representative of our cavalier attitude toward noise as a concomitant of "progress" is the recent Presidential go-ahead for the supersonic transport. It is now asserted that the SST, whose usefulness and cost-benefit ratio are debatable even without considering the inevitable sonic boom, will be permitted to fly supersonically only over water. The resulting limitation of boom effects (although not takeoff and landing noise) to fisherman, island dwellers and oceanic travelers is another demonstration of our remarkable ability to endure the acute discomfort of someone else. The world perspective which must be acquired if a livable environment is to be preserved is obviously not yet at hand.

One-shot Assaults

Thermonuclear War

Most of us are aware of the possibility that thermonuclear war will cause more destruction in an hour than man's prolonged insults to the environment could manage in decades. Nevertheless, since some strategic planners continue to argue that such a war is "survivable" and hence a viable policy alternative, it is worth reviewing some pertinent facts. The strategists seem to base their arguments on calculations of the number of millions of people who might survive blast and short-term radiation effects in various postulated attacks. Unfortunately, their projections overlook or underestimate ecological and sociological effects which, in the aftermath of a nuclear war, could easily result in the complete demise of civilized man.

Consider the effects of a rather limited exchange among the United States, Russia, China, and various European powers. The flow of food and technological aid from the developed to the underdeveloped nations would cease instantaneously. In the absence of the wheat, seeds, fertilizers, and mechanical equipment previously supplied by the now-devastated countries, much of the unscathed but also undeveloped world would promptly be pitched into massive famines. Blast effects and huge fires burning in the warring nations would fill the atmosphere with debris. The resulting reduction of sunlight for at least a year thereafter would significantly lower the mean surface temperature of the earth, compounding famines by reducing agricultural production still further.

The direct effects of the blasts and fires themselves possibly have been badly underestimated. Germany's experiences with firestorms several square miles in area during World War II presage such catastrophes in much greater dimensions in the event of a nuclear conflict. Individual firestorms, generating extreme temperatures, might then incinerate hundreds or thousands of square miles apiece in forest or metropolitan areas. Not only would vegetation be removed, but vast areas of soil might be sterilized. Rains washing away the unprotected top soil would then ensure the permanent loss of productivity of much of the hemisphere's agricultural land, and the silt and radioactive debris deposited in the process in the fragile offshore waters would wreak havoc on ocean fisheries.

In short, in the face of widespread famine, soaring disease and mutation rates from radioactive fallout, raging epidemics in the absence of much of the world's medical technology, and generally harsher environmental conditions than man has ever faced before, it is problematical whether the survivors of even "limited" thermonuclear war will survive for very long. It is not our intention here to delve into the correlation between population pressures and the probability that such a conflict will occur; it suffices to point out that few students of the psychology and economics of war dispute the connection.

Epidemics: Natural and Man-made

The present world population is not only large, crowded, and malnourished beyond precedent, it is also the most mobile the world has ever seen. People, potential carriers of disease of every description, move routinely and in substantial numbers from continent to continent in matters of hours. Thus the potential for worldwide epidemic has never been greater, notwithstanding the popular belief that modern medicine has made such a catastrophe impossible.

Consider, in this connection, the difficulty experienced in the United States in coping with the relatively mild Asian flu epidemic in 1968. It proved impossible to manufacture and distribute enough vaccine in time to protect most of the population. That relatively few deaths were associated with the epidemic was not owing to modern public health measures; this particular virus happened to be nonfatal for victims in otherwise good health. Our knowledge of viruses, although incomplete, is sufficient to indicate that the spontaneous development of highly lethal strains is possible—in other words, we may not be so lucky the next time.

Another area in which we might not remain lucky is the transfer of lethal viruses from animal populations to man. Recently a new virus, the Marburgvirus, was transmitted from green monkeys to workers in a German laboratory. Among 32 people contracting this highly contagious disease there were six deaths. Only the appearance of the disease in a medically sophisticated environment permitted its containment and minimized the number of deaths. If the virus had escaped into the population at large (the monkeys had been in the London Airport on their way to Marburg) a billion deaths might possibly have occurred.

We have already witnessed the vulnerability of our highly mechanized society to such comparatively minor disruptions as power blackouts and snow storms. One can perhaps imagine, then, the almost total societal breakdown which could result from a serious epidemic. Millions of vital jobs would go unattended, while still healthy individuals fled the cities to avoid infection. Such consequences of the disease itself would seriously impede the use of any ameliorative measures which happened to be available.

In many parts of the world, health conditions with the potential for initiating such a disaster are worsening. Rats thriving on stored grain in India have revived the spectre of bubonic plague there. The serious parasitic disease, bilharzia, is spreading across Egypt through new irrigation canals connected with the Aswan High Dam project. And wholesale use of chemotherapy and antibiotics has resulted in the development of resistant strains of bacteria and other parasites. The same conditions of crowding, malnourishment, and mobility which make mankind so vulnerable to epidemic also magnify the potential consequences of chemical and biological warfare. Chemical Biological Warfare (CBW) is, unfortunately, the poor man's atomic bomb—a few dollars and one or two trained microbiologists can put any country in the business of developing its own biological doomsday weapons. The possibilities are abundant: drug-resistant strains of known diseases, new ways to transmit old foes (such as rabies), altogether new viruses, and chemical or biological attacks on food supplies, to name a few. One can hope that the world's arsenals of such material will never be used. But even if they are not, the abundant potential for accidents remains (it has already been demonstrated in this country at Skull Valley, Utah, where the victims happened to be sheep). Surely there are more pleasant, if less comprehensive, solutions to overpopulation.

Man-made Earthquakes

Man has already demonstrated the ability to trigger inadvertently the release of vast amounts of destructive energy stored in the stress field of the earth. His most long-standing activity of this sort is the construction of large dams, whose enormous reservoirs result in substantial loading of the earth's crust. When Lake Mead was first filled during the period from 1935 to 1939, thousands of seismic events were recorded in that previously inactive area. The largest earthquake involved had a magnitude of 5 on the Richter scale. Other dams in relatively inactive regions of the world have caused numerous earthquakes with magnitudes greater than 6—sufficient to do substantial damage to urban areas. A quake registering 6.4, associated with the filling of the Kogna Dam in India, was responsible for 200 fatalities in 1967.

Underground nuclear explosions provide another potential means for achieving similar results. The fact that the recent Amchitka test did not induce a major quake proves nothing but the good fortune of everyone involved. It must be emphasized that stresses associated with either reservoirs or nuclear explosions may act as *triggers* and not as the principal source of energy for an earthquake (although a nuclear explosion itself can have an equivalent magnitude of 6 or 7). There is therefore no reason to expect that a much larger quake than any associated with these causes to date will not eventually result. The consequences of the associated earth movement and possible tidal waves will of course be directly proportional to the number of people crammed onto the world at the time.

Subtle Assaults: Chipping Away at the "Invisible Environment"

Persistent Pesticides and Other Chemicals

Instances of the poisoning of important food fishes and birds of prey by chlorinated hydrocarbon pesticides were given in the previous section. Probably much more dangerous are long-term effects which cannot yet be measured in numbers of corpses; damning evidence that it will come to that is accumulating steadily. The alarming distribution of DDT and its relatives is accounted for by their mobility, by the long time period over which these compounds remain intact before being degraded by natural processes, and by their solubility in fat. The first property means that the compounds move easily from the places where they are deposited. They vaporize into the atmosphere, cling to moving dust particles, and move along with ground water, et cetera. The second property—a half-life of a decade or more—means that the substances remain active during and after their dispersal by wind and water over the entire face of the earth. The third property promotes the movement of these compounds from the nonliving environment into living systems, all of which have fatty components. This leads to their accumulation at increasing concentrations as they move up the biological food chains— from plant to herbivore to carnivore to secondary carnivore, and so on. The mass of organisms at each trophic (feeding) level is constrained by the laws of thermodynamics to be less than the mass on the next lower level. In terms of a simple example, this means that it may take 100 pounds of grass to make ten pounds of steer, which in turn may be used to make a pound of man (here, the third trophic level). But while only 10% of the grass itself ends up as steer, a much higher percentage of the DDT *on* the grass does, because it tends to dissolve in the first fat it encounters, and little DDT is lost as energy and materials pass from trophic level to trophic level. In food chains with many trophic levels, such as many aquatic ones, such fat-soluble pesticides may be concentrated to thousands of times their initial environmental levels. Even at low trophic levels, filter feeding organisms such as oysters may build up astonishingly high concentrations.

These mechanisms explain why pesticide levels in lake-dwelling plankton were found in a representative instance to be 250 times the concentration of application (to control gnats). The concentrations in frogs, sunfish and fish-eating birds inhabiting the same lake were, respectively, 2,000, 12,000 and 80,000 times that of the application. Equally ominous, the intake of DDT by infants around the globe is now about twice the maximum recommended by the World Health Organization. In adult humans, DDT is often found at concentrations of 12 parts per million (ppm) in fat. In mother's milk, concentrations of 0.2 ppm are not unusual; for comparison, we note that the permissible levels in cow's milk is set by the Federal Drug Administration (FDA) at 0.05 ppm.

The producers of persistent pesticides argue that these levels are harmless and cite two poorly designed studies of adults exposed to heavy doses of DDT over several years. The fact that none of the subjects displayed symptoms of acute poisoning during the observation period is not particularly reassuring; by the same criteria, cigarette smoking and fallout would also be judged perfectly safe. Against this shaky evidence are arrayed innumerable studies of the toxic effects of DDT and other pesticides on various animals: DDT in large doses increases incidence of cancer in mice (similar evidence on cyclamates recently resulted in an FDA ban); DDT interferes with the reproductive physiology of rats, which resembles that of humans; various chlorinated hydrocarbons can cause abnormal changes in animal brain wave patterns, and trout exposed to 20 ppm DDT lose the ability to learn to avoid electric shock.

Evidence of long-term pernicious effects on human beings is just beginning to come in, some twenty years after the introduction of DDT (how long did it take to get the goods on cigarettes?). Perhaps the most significant recent study correlated high fat concentrations of DDT and its breakdown products with human deaths from softening of the brain, cerebral hemorrhage, hypertension, cirrhosis of the liver, and various cancers. These results are only preliminary, but they are ominous. Finally, it should be noted that we have no experience with the effects of DDT over a typical human lifespan—the first people to have been exposed to DDT from conception are now only in their early twenties.

Nevertheless, the persistent pesticides pose a far greater threat than the rather direct one to man's health—they have the potential to undermine the food production of both land and sea. As regards the sea, DDT at a few parts per billion concentration has been shown to inhibit photosynthesis in phytoplankton, the tiny green plants which are at the bottom of the ocean food pyramid. Again the results are preliminary but frightening. If photosynthesis in the ocean as a whole were affected, the total amount of food available to man from that source would diminish correspondingly. Far more likely than the *end* of photosynthesis in phytoplankton is a rise to dominance of some particular form which is *least* susceptible to the low concentrations of DDT (less than one part per billion) in most seawater today. This could lead to huge "blooms" of one species or another, with serious consequences throughout the oceanic food chains. Or it could lead to a change in the size of the dominant phytoplankton species—an occurrence which could dramatically decrease fisheries' yields. In this entire area, mankind is operating largely from a position of ignorance; scientific knowledge has barely scratched the complexities of the life and chemistry of the sea. But such facts as are available suggest that the potential for man-induced disaster is there.

We are on equally uncertain ground in regard to the effects of pesticides on topsoil. As was pointed out in an earlier section, soil is a complicated biological community in itself. Its continued fertility is dependent, among other things, on the unhindered operation of natural cycles involving nitrogen, carbon, and phosphorous. All these cycles depend in part on living organisms—bacteria, fungi, and others—whose defenses against the long-lived pesticides now accumulating in soils everywhere is a matter of conjecture. The nitrogen cycle is particularly vulnerable, being in several essential steps *completely* dependent on certain bacteria. It has been said, perhaps only slightly overstating the case, that the extermination of any of several of these crucial populations would mean the end of life on earth.

Nor are pesticides the only slow-acting poisons with which we are lacing the environment. Some, like lead, are not merely persistent, they do not degrade at all. Symptoms of chronic lead poisoning in humans include miscarriage, weakness, and lesions in various parts of the circulatory, digestive, and nervous systems (it doesn't miss much). Such descriptions are particularly discouraging in view of the fact that the atmospheric lead level from all sources (including gasoline additives, smelting, lead piping, and lead-bearing paints, ceramics and glassware) increased some 400% between 1750 and 1940 and another 300% between 1940 and 1967. There is considerable disagreement about what level of lead can be tolerated by humans without substantial ill effects. Because lead is a *cummulative* cellular poison, it seems unwise to wait until everyone is displaying symptoms before attempting to reduce its concentration in the environment.

We remain uncertain of all the consequences of lead in ecological systems, although its effects on people should give even the biologically uninitiated a clue. Nevertheless, as a result of man's activities some 100,000 tons of lead particles fall into the oceans every year, and the lead concentration in the Pacific is up by a factor of 10 since the first gasoline additives were introduced 45 years ago. It should be noted in this connection that lead, like pesticides, concentrates heavily along food chains.

Many other industrial metals form toxic compounds—nickel is one; and it, too, has been added to gasoline. Altogether, it is estimated that man is putting about half a million different pollutants into the ocean, and about three thousand into the air. The associated risks, already monumental, will increase as proliferating populations demand—and dispose of—more of everything.

Radiation

Radioactive substances are those which undergo spontaneous changes in nuclear structure accompanied by the emission of energetic particles and, usually, penetrating electromagnetic waves. The latter, called gamma rays, are identical to X rays of equal energy in every respect except origin. The particles (principally helium nuclei and electrons), the gamma rays, and X rays are all lumped under the term "radiation." The debilitating or lethal effects of acute doses of radiation—such as those associated with nuclear warfare or with serious accidents in the handling of nuclear reactors and isotopes—have been well publicized, and we shall not discuss them here.

The dangers of prolonged, low-level exposures to radiation are more insidious and have some similarity to those of pesticides: the absence of immediate and obvious symptoms does not imply that the exposure is harmless; radioactive substances remain dangerous for extended lengths of time; and many are concentrated in biological systems. The differences of degree, however, are very important ones. For example, the half-lives of two particularly dangerous fission products, strontium 90 and cesium 137, are about 30 years; and because of the potency of these substances a nominal initial amount of either remains hazardous for centuries. Indeed, if lethality is given its customary definition as destructive effect per unit of energy released in tissue, radiation is 100,000,000 times as deadly as cyanide.

Radiation from cosmic rays and from radioactive material in the earth's crust has always been with us. It amounts to an average of from 0.08 to 0.15 rads per person per year. (The rad is the customary unit of absorbed ionizing radiation, and amounts to 100 ergs of energy per gram of absorber.) There is a great temptation to regard this so-called background level of radiation as a yardstick for safety, in particular, to regard any man-made increment of radiation as safe if, averaged over the exposed population, it is smaller than or comparable to the natural background. There are three flaws in this approach. First, available evidence indicates that *no* amount of ionizing radiation, not even the relatively low background, is completely safe—some mutations are always induced, and if the exposed population is large enough and the data complete enough a statistical increase in deformities, stillbirths, and cancers will always appear. (In the case of natural background radiation, there is no unexposed "control" group for comparison; however, it is reasonable to suppose that a historical burden of mutations, although small, has been associated with the background.) The second flaw arises because (with respect to genetic effects), at least, radiation doses are cumulative—a given man-induced dose must be considered in combination with all other sources of exposure, natural and artificial, past, present, and future. The third flaw stems from the frequent assumption that the dose can be determined essentially by dividing the total radioactivity involved (measured in nuclear disintegrations per second) by the area of the part of the planet exposed. The biological concentration of many radioactive substances makes nonsense of this assumption.

There will be some environmental and human cost associated with *any* increase in radiation dose, just as such costs accrue from the consumption of gasoline, the use of pesticides and fertilizers, and so on. The pertinent question in every case is: at what point do the incremental penalties outweigh the incremental gain? The peculiar problem with radiation is that the penalties are so far removed in time from the activity and its benefits. By the time the price is clear, the damage is done.

Standards for "permissible" radiation exposure vary somewhat among the various national and international agencies which promulgate them. Nor can the standards be easily summarized, for they specify not only a variety of absorbed doses depending on occupation, length of exposure, and organs exposed, but they also fix maximum environmental concentrations for a vast assortment of isotopes of varying biological effectiveness. Two numbers which are representative are the International Commission for Radiation Protection's recommendations of no more than 5 rads accumulated total in the first 30 years of life (0.17 rads/year average) for the general population, and 5 rads/year for workers in X-ray and nuclear technology (both these figures refer to radiation in excess of the natural background). Unfortunately, many of the guidelines in use today were last substantially revised in the fifties; prominent scientists affiliated with nuclear programs in the United States have recently suggested that, in view of recent knowledge, some of these levels may be ten times too high. It is true that, *on average* exposures have not yet approached the guideline levels; but there is reason to believe they will. And individual and local overdoses are already innumerable.

At the moment, by far the bulk of man-made radiation exposure is attributable to medical and dental X-ray equipment—over 90%—and the vast majority of radiation-induced deaths are caused by these sources. A single pelvic X-ray examination to determine the position of a fetus delivers 1.3 rads to the mother and 2.7 to the unborn child, appreciably increasing the probability that the child will eventually contract leukemia. X-ray leakage from color television sets is becoming a non-negligible source of exposure for many Americans, and even a radioactive wristwatch may cause an exposure of up to 0.6 rad/year (mostly to relatively insensitive parts of the body).

Potentially the most serious radiation threat related to population growth is the proliferation of nuclear reactors for the generation of electric power. The highly concentrated radioactive wastes produced by these reactors have been the subject of much study and concern. Although there is cause for uneasiness in the present disposition of these wastes (which remain dangerous for hundreds of years and more) in underground tanks and, at more moderate concentrations, in concrete-lined barrels at the bottom of the sea, the Atomic Energy Commission's proposal to store them in the future in abandoned salt mines seems sound. Far more bothersome are the comparatively small amounts of radioactive isotopes which are released to air and water at virtually every step of the nuclear power production process—from mining and processing the fuel, to running the reactor, to transporting and reprocessing the spent fuel elements. Because of the low concentrations of the substances involved, their control and removal is technically difficult and correspondingly expensive. And because price is the name of the game in power production, there is a temptation to encourage standards based more on what is economically feasible than on what is biologically acceptable.

Today's standards on the emission of radioactive pollutants at the various steps in power production are often applied on a one-installation-at-a-time philosophy: if the anticipated levels of radiation from a single facility do not pose a clear hazard to health, such levels are judged safe. As we have pointed out above, such an approach is inconsistent with much of our knowledge about radioactive substances and radiation—particularly the concentration of some of the isotopes in biological systems and the existence of additive destructive effects from radiation of all origins. The consequences of this philosophy are not yet pronounced because the number of facilities is still small (although local violations of even today's overgenerous standards have occasionally occurred). But if nuclear power plants undergo the hundredfold or greater proliferation predicted for them, and if the present concept of "safe" is not revised, the consequences may be totally unacceptable. If the concept *is* revised, the cost of meeting the more realistic standards will slow the proliferation.

As with pesticides, the threat of radiation overdoses may be even more severe for the environmental life-support systems than for the physical health of man. The effects of radioactive isotopes on many of the organisms which concentrate them are incompletely known. The long-term consequences of further irradiating the microorganisms which provide the fertility of the soil and sea are largely matters of speculation. Because of the additivity and longevity of radiation damage, once we go too far there will be no turning back the clock.

The Alteration of Climate

Numerous inspired publicity agents for science have long made glowing statements about control of the weather—the individual occurrences of rain and snow, sunshine and clouds, tornadoes and hurricanes, which taken together comprise the climate. Nevertheless, an inspection of the batting average of weather forecasters suggests that our ability to predict, much less control, the weather is still in its infancy. It is therefore both remarkable and disconcerting to discover that the activities of man are unintentionally altering climate and weather not only locally (as in ground fogs from cooling towers and inversion changes over cities) but also globally.

The global situation is of course of greater significance, and while it is still only poorly understood, a semblance of an explanation can be given. The surface temperature of the earth is determined by a heat balance, a simplified version of which is as follows: incident energy from the sun, largely in the visible part of the electromagnetic spectrum, warms the surface of the earth and drives the winds, ocean currents, water cycle, photosynthesis and so on. These processes in themselves lead to the dissipation of heat, which, together with that absorbed directly by the earth from the sun, is re-radiated outward in the infrared part of the spectrum. Substantial interference by man with any part of this process can result in changing the average surface temperature and hence the climate.

Such interference currently takes several forms. One is the steady increase of the carbon dioxide content of the atmosphere, believed to be due primarily to increasing combustion of hydrocarbon fuels. Carbon dioxide is essentially transparent to incoming visible light, so it doesn't change the input to the heat balance; but being opaque to part of the outbound infrared energy, it does reduce the amount of heat which can escape. This effect, if it were the only one operating, would result in a warming trend. (Glass has similar properties which account for the warmth of a greenhouse—and for the name "greenhouse effect" appied to the CO_2 phenomenon.)

It seems, however, that a competing effect has dominated the situation since 1940. This is the reduced transparency of the atmosphere to incoming light as a result of urban air pollution (smoke, aerosols) and agricultural air pollution (dust). This screening phenomenon is said to be responsible for the present world cooling trend—a total of about 0.2°C in the world mean surface temperature over the past quarter century. This number seems small until it is realized that a decrease of only 4°C would propably be sufficient to start another ice age. Moreover, other effects besides simple screening by air pollution threaten to move us in the same direction. In particular, a mere 1% increase in low cloud cover would decrease the surface temperature by 0.8°C. We are in the process of providing just such a cloud increase, and more, by adding man-made condensation nuclei to the atmosphere in the form of jet exhausts and other suitable pollutants. A final push in the cooling direction comes from man-made changes in the direct reflectivity of the earth's surface (albedo) through urbanization, deforestation, and the enlargement of deserts.

The effects of a new ice age on agriculture and the supportability of large human populations scarcely need elaboration here. Even more dramatic results are possible, however, for instance, a sudden outward slumping in the Antarctic ice cap, induced by added weight, could generate a tidal wave of proportions unprecedented in recorded history.

If man survives the comparatively short-term threat of making the planet too cold, there is every indication he is quite capable of making it too warm not long thereafter. For the remaining major means of interference with the global heat balance is the release of energy from fossil and nuclear fuels. As pointed out previously, all this energy is ultimately degraded to heat. What are today scattered local effects of its disposition will in time, with the continued growth of population and energy consumption, give way to global warming. The present rate of increase of energy use, if continued, will bring us in about seventy-five years to the point where our heat input could have drastic global consequences. Again, the exact form such consequences might take is unknown; the melting of the icecaps with a concomitant 150-foot increase in sea level might be one of them.

Ecosystem Destabilization

A common thread runs through the discussion in this section on "subtle" assaults on the environment—that thread is the utter inadequacy of man's knowledge in the face of the problems he confronts. For many of the most serious difficulties involve the effects of substances or phenomena we do not understand very well (pesticides, radiation, air pollution) on systems we do not understand very well either (soil microorganisms, ocean food chains, climate). What is becoming clear is that man's activities are modifying the planet so extensively that the natural stability of the ecosystems we inherited is imperiled. The crime we are committing is the destruction of the life support systems of our planetary spaceship, the death of our environment, in short—ecocide.

The ecosystem concept means no less than the totality of the biological community, the physical environment in which these organisms exist, and the intricate web of relationships which interconnects the whole. It is the very complexity of the interrelationships which imparts stability to the ecosystem—the existence of many alternative links in a food chain ensures the success of the enterprise even if the population of a species or two declines or explodes; the presence of many alternative paths in a mineral cycle serves the same function. A complex forest or jungle community may persist for centuries (in the absence of interference by man); by contrast, a simple cornfield is subject to instant ruin if not vigilantly protected.

Mankind, even since before the agricultural revolution, has been a simplifier of the ecosystem. He has decimated species and, both literally and figuratively, replaced the forests with cornfields. Today, with his pesticides, radiation and miscellaneous pollution, he threatens to remove altogether links whose functions he does not even understand. He is by the entire process inevitably pushing the world toward instability.

In this analysis, we have considered threats to various components of the ecosystem as if those components were separate entities. They are not, of course, and neither are the threats. A discouraging concept in this regard is that of synergistic interaction, in which the effect of two causes operating together is greater than the sum of their effects if they operated separately. Some examples of known or probable synergisms are enhanced toxicity of benzyprene and sulfur dioxide when the two are present together, and the interaction of asbestos particles with smoking and other air pollutants in accelerating lung disease. Possible synergisms between pesticides and air pollution or pesticides and radiation are fertile areas for speculation.

In summary, we want to say that the direct threats to health which result from man's activities in support of his ever-growing population are many. But the threats which the same activities pose to the systems on which *all* life depends are still more numerous—and less well understood. It is a safe assumption that as population continues to grow, and as technology is pressed harder and harder to devise means to cope with more and more people, more frequent and more serious mistakes will be made. Even the mistakes already with us are aggravated simply because they are made on behalf of so many people, and because so many people are here to be affected.

It is remarkable that nature's systems—plant communities, mineral cycles, food chains—become more stable with increasing complexity, while man's systems (cities, power grids, instruments of defense and war) appear to grow less stable as their complexity increases. It should worry us more than it does that we are pushing *both* in the wrong direction.

Simple arithmetic makes it plain that indefinite population growth in the finite space allotted to us is impossible. In this chapter we have posed the cost-benefit question several times in regard to different activities; we pose it once more with respect to the concept of the previous sentence: What is gained and what is lost in the pursuit of the impossible? We have enumerated here the possible costs—they include the destruction of all life on this planet. Where is the gain that justifies this risk?

Paul R. Ehrlich is Professor of Biology at Stanford University, where he has been a member of the faculty since 1959. He has authored or edited several books and more than 80 papers on entomology, evolution, and population biology, including the best-selling paperback, *The Population Bomb.* His most recent book is *Population, Resources, Environment* , a text coauthored with his wife, Anne.

A graduate of the University of Pennsylvania, Professor Ehrlich received his M.A. and Ph.D. degrees from the University of Kansas. He has conducted field research in Colorado, Alaska, Mexico, the Canadian arctic and subarctic, Australia, New Guinea, New Britain, the Solomon Islands, Malaya, Cambodia, India, Kashmir, and East Africa. He is a fellow of the California Academy of Sciences, an Honorary Life Member of the American Museum of Natural History, a member-at-large of the Governing Board of the American Institute of Biological Sciences, and an Associate of the Center for the Study of Democratic Institutions.

John P. Holdren is a physicist in the controlled thermonuclear fusion division at the University of California's Lawrence Radiation Laboratory in Livermore. He has published in his professional field of plasma physics and, with Dr. Ehrlich, in the areas of population, resources, and environment. Dr. Holdren has lectured widely on the interaction of technology with the population/environment crisis. He is a member of the International Environmental Programs Committee of the National Academy of Sciences.

Dr. Holdren received his B.S. and M.S. degree in Aeronautics and Astronautics at the Massachusetts Institute of Technology, and his Ph.D. in an inter-departmental program in plasma physics at Stanford University.

CHAPTER 3

The Ecologist's Role
And The Nonsolution of
Technology

William Murdoch
Joseph Connell

> *The sonic boom 'problem', of course, cannot* IN PRIN—
> CIPLE *be 'solved'* . . . *The job of the ecologist is to*
> *dispel this faith in technology.*

There suddenly has appeared a widely held belief that ecologists have a great deal to say about the relationship between the ecologist and the environmental crisis. We concur with this belief, and therefore it is crucial to get a clear understanding of the nature both of ecology and of the environmental crisis.

Ecologists function at two conceptual levels. The first level is directly concerned with their day-to-day research, and the second constitutes a way of viewing the world. We contend that the nature of the crisis is such that the second kind of ecological thinking is the more significant, and that it determines the kind of solution ecologists (and others) should press for in solving the environmental crisis in the United States—and for that matter, on a global basis. One of our major theses is that this solution is different in kind from the sort of solution which we believe the public generally expects.

The public's awakening to the environmental crisis has been quite remarkable over the past few years. A recent Gallup poll showed that about half of the United States citizens were aware of—and concerned about—the population problem. A questionnaire sent to approximately 500 students in freshman biology for nonmajors at the University of California, Santa Barbara, asked which of 25 topics should be included in a general biology course for nonmajors. The top four positions were: Human Population Problem (85%), Genetics (71.3%) and Ecology (66%).

Another change is that the average citizen is at least getting to know the right words, even though his basic understanding may not be significantly increased. Not more than four or five years ago we had to explain at length what an ecologist was when people asked about our jobs, but recently the word ecologist has been met with a knowing and almost respectful nod. This is both a good and a potentially dangerous change.

It is true also that a change has occurred among ecologists themselves. Until recently ecologists' meetings had concerned themselves with the usual esoterica. Suddenly ecologists have departed from this presentation of "pure science" and harangued each other on the necessity of ecologists becoming involved in the "real world."

We believe that a profound and lasting change has occurred in a large number of ecologists, and that this will have a major effect upon their activities—and hence upon the nation and the environment. The change for one particular ecologist is very well described by C.S. Holling in an issue of *Time* * in which that magazine recognized the existence of the environment. A trend has started which no doubt will increase over the years. At last the obscure ecologist has been summoned to Washington. In the future we can expect that the peripatetic "ecological expert" will join the ranks of consultants jetting back and forth to the capitol, thereby (unfortunately) adding their quota of pollution to the atmosphere. However, that will be a small price to pay if the ecologists can clear the air of the misconception and political verbiage that passes for an environmental policy in Washington.

Concern about the environment is not limited to the United States, and indeed the ecological crisis—by its nature—is basically an international problem. Evidence of international concern abounds, and the plans of the Center for the Study of Democratic Institutions for fostering international discussion of the issue is one of the more hopeful signs of the times. So it seems likely that the ecologist as *expert* is here to stay.

To some extent the present commotion about ecology arises from people pressing to get on the bandwagon; and when the limits of ecological expertise become apparent, we must expect to lose a few passengers. But, if only because there is no alternative, the ecologist and the policymakers appear to be stuck with each other for some time to come.

While a growing awareness of the relevance of ecology must be welcomed, there are already misconceptions about the field. And further, the traditional role of the expert in Washington predisposes the nation to a misuse of its ecologists. The reasons for our concern about this can be illustrated by an example. A common lament of the socially conscious citizen is that we have enough science and technology to put a

Time Magazine, "Environment," August 15, 1969.

man on the moon, but we cannot maintain a decent environment in the United States. The implicit premise seems clear: it is that the solution to our ecological crisis is a *technological* one, and a logical extension of this argument is that in this particular case the ecologist is the appropriate scientist or "engineer" to solve the crisis. This reflects the dominant American philosophy (which always comes up when one lectures in public on the subject of the environment) that the answer to our problem is technology, and in particular that the answer to the problems raised by technology is more technology. Perhaps the most astounding example of this blind faith is the recent assurance issued by the government that the SST will not fly over the United States *until the sonic-boom problem is solved!* The sonic boom "problem," of course, cannot in principle be "solved." Our thesis, in brief, is that the job of the ecologist is to dispel this faith in technology.

We believe that an analogy can be drawn between the environment and the war in Vietnam which is instructive of a rather general approach our society uses to problems. In Vietnam the United States—possibly for the first time in its history—has arrived at a situation where a political problem cannot be solved by the application of more military might, just as (we believe) the ecological crisis can no longer be solved by more technology. The parallel is closer than that. In Vietnam the problem has arisen directly from the application of military power, and each renewed effort by the military machine bogs it down further in the morass of its own making. Such pie-in-the-sky "final solutions"—like the bombing of Haiphong—will not miraculously solve a problem which requires a political solution. Similarly, a giant technological leap—such as the massive use of nuclear power—will not solve our environmental problem, for this too is basically a problem requiring a political solution—or at least a change in values.

There are two examples of how the growth of population, combined with the increasing power and sophistication of technology, have caused crises in the environment. Planning based on foresight might have prevented these and other crises. But the fact is that no application of technology to solve problems caused by increased population has ever considered the consequences to the environment.

The first example is the Aswan High Dam on the upper Nile.* Its purposes were laudable—to provide a regular supply of water for irrigation, to prevent disastrous floods, and to provide electrical power to a primitive society. Other effects were not taken into account. The annual flood of the Nile brought a supply of rich nutrients to the eastern Mediterranean Sea, renewing its fertility. Fishermen have long depended

*George, Carl J., "The Influence of the New Aswan High Dam (U.A.R.) on the Ecology of the Eastern Mediterranean—A Preliminary Study." *Environment 11 (1):* 31-32. 1969.

upon this annual cycle. Since the Aswan Dam has stopped the annual flood with its load of nutrients, the annual bloom of phytoplankton in the eastern Mediterranean does not occur. Thus the food chain from phytoplankton to zooplankton to fish has been broken, and the sardine fishery—once producing 18,000 tons per year (about half of the total fish catch)—has dropped to about 500 tons per year.

A second ecological effect of the dam has been to replace an intermittent flowing stream with a permanent stable lake. This has allowed aquatic snails to maintain large populations, whereas before the dam was built they had been reduced each year during the dry season. Because irrigation supports a larger human population, there are now many more people living close to these stable bodies of water. The problem is that the snails serve as intermediate hosts of the larvae of a blood fluke. The larvae leave the snail and bore into humans, infecting the liver and other organs, and cause the disease schistosomiasis. The species of snail which live in stable water harbor a more virulent specie of fluke than the one which lives in another species of snail in running water. Thus the lake behind the Aswan has increased both the incidence and virulence of the disease in the people of the upper Nile.

Will these lessons be learned and applied to further plans for construction of dams in underdeveloped countries? Judging by plans* now underway for an even larger dam across the Amazon, the answer is *no*. Several low dams would create an inland sea one-third the size of France, thereby opening up for exploitation an area about the size of the United States, and providing great amounts of hydroelectric power. The entire ecological insight in the article is distilled into the following passage:

> Among the risks to be considered is significant disruption of the ecological balance of the area. *Ecological problems are not usually significant in terms of a country the size of Brazil* but the inland sea is so large that some surprises are probable. The Atlantic currents that flow north to the Caribbean and United States receive minerals from the sediment-choked outflow of the Amazon, most of which would be stopped by the dam. What effect would this lack of minerals have on fishing off Florida? The question is difficult to answer, even with intense study, as one might miss something significant. Another risk is the inland sea's effect on climate in the area. *We would expect none of these risks, though, to prevent construction of the dam. Such risks are present in all dams and reservoirs and have never really prevented any from being built.*

The final statement, which is no doubt accurate, is a remarkable summary of our previous attitude to the environment. It is also extraordinary that this is the only recognition in the article of possible ecological consequences.

*Panero, Robert B., "A Dam Across the Amazon," *Science Journal 5A(3)*: 56-60. 1969.

Our second example is the effect of chlorinated hydrocarbon pesticides, particularly DDT, on the environment.* The pesticide DDT has
the following characteristics. It is only slightly soluble in water, so that
it is carried mainly on particles in water for short distances until the
particles settle out. But on tiny particles in the atmosphere it is carried
great distances, and it may even fall out more heavily in distant places
than close to the point where it was sprayed. DDT is not readily broken
down by microorganisms, so it persists in the environment for many
years. It is very soluble in fats so that it is quickly taken up by organisms. Because herbivores eat many times their own weight of plants but
do not break down the DDT, it accumulates in their bodies. This accumulated DDT is further concentrated in carnivores eating many individual herbivores, so that the species at the top of food chains end up with
high doses of DDT in their tissues. Evidence is accumulating that certain species of predators, such as peregrine falcons and pelicans, are
being wiped out as a result of physiological debilities, which lead to
reproductive failure caused by accumulations of DDT.

The tendency of DDT to kill both the herbivores "pest" and also its
predators has produced some unpredicted consequences. Hebivores are
often kept at rather low numbers by their predators, with occasional
"outbreaks" when there is a decrease in these enemies. When spraying is
started it often kills both the pests and their natural enemies, so the
pests are continually able to increase and spraying must be continued. In
two instances, in cotton fields in Peru and in cocoa plantations in Malay-
sia, the situation got so bad that pesticides spraying was stopped. Natural enemies then increased, and the damage by pests has diminished to
the former tolerable levels.

However, not all cases have such happy endings. The reproduction of
top carnivores such as ospreys and pelicans is being reduced to negligible amounts, which will cause their extinction. No amount of ingenuity can reconstruct a species of osprey once extinct. Species lower in the
food chain are more abundant and reproduce faster. The chances are
that a few of them will possess some hereditary resistance to any particular insecticide. If so, these will be the ones surviving to breed. After
doses of DDT these resistant strains will increase greatly in the absence
of competitors and enemies. This is an example of evolution in action.
Because DDT is not present in concentrated form in the environment it
does not represent an energy resource common enough to support a
microorganism, so that none has yet evolved the ability to break it
down—even though it has been sprayed for 25 years.

In summary, the indiscriminate use of DDT throughout the world, its
dispersal by the atmosphere, its property of killing both pests and their
enemies, and the evolution of resistant strains—all have combined to

*Frost, Justin, "Earth, Air, Water," *Environment 11(6)*: 14-33. 1969.

create a crisis in the environment. The reaction has been to stop spraying in some crops, and to ban its use in some countries. Probably the correct solution is to use pesticides carefully, apply them locally (by hand if possible) to places where pest outbreaks are threatening, and try to introduce or encourage enemies of the pests. This is called "integrated control," and it is the hope of the future. As yet there is very little known about how the abundance of organisms is controlled in natural populations—so ecologists have their work cut out for them.

Ecologists are concerned with such problems as controlling pests and maximizing the yield from populations. Ecologists (we have in mind pure ecologists, and in particular population and community ecologists) study interactions among individuals in a population of organisms, among populations and between populations and their environments. A population is a more or less well-defined group of organisms which belong to the same species.

A brief indication of how the "professional" ecologist spends his time may be in order. One of us (Connell) is interested in discovering what determines the distribution on the rocky seashore of a species of barnacle. He makes frequent visits to the shore, photographs the positions of barnacles, counts their numbers at different levels on the shore at different life stages, notes the density and positions of predators, other barnacles species, et cetera. He develops a hypothesis (in one area that the limit to distribution is set by the presence of another barnacle species, in another area that beyond a certain height on the seashore a snail species eats them all) and tests the idea by doing experiments. These experiments consist of placing cages on the shore to exclude predators, removing the competing species, et cetera. This work has gone on for fourteen years and has firmly established the two hypotheses.

In contrast, the other (Murdoch) has spent the past three years in the laboratory examining an idea about predators. The idea is that predators keep the number of their various prey species stable by attacking very heavily whichever species is most abundant. (The idea is a bit more complicated than that, but that is approximately it.) This has entailed setting up experiments where different predators were offered different mixtures of two prey species at a variety of densities, and then counting the number eaten of each species. These experiments led to others to test different subhypotheses. The conclusion was that predators would "switch," as the idea indicated, only under very particular conditions.

Other ecologists spend long periods in the field trying to measure what happens, for example, to the vegetable material in the field. How much is produced, what percentage goes to rabbits, mice, insects? What percentage of the total weight of mice produced (biomass) is eaten by weasels, and how efficient are weasels at converting mice biomass to weasel biomass? Such work takes a great deal of time, estimates are rough, shaky assumptions have to be made, and in the end we have only approximate answers. Other ecologists think while reclining in arm-chairs, taking sauna baths, playing gin-rummy, or doing a variety of other things as they try to build mathematical models which will suggest how a community—or some subset of a community—comes to have the structure which their rough measurements tell them it may have.

Ecologists' reasons for indulging in their many activities are the same as those of any scientist. They hope to build models of how nature works—models which, while not being copies of nature, will catch the essence of some process in nature and serve as a basis for explaining the observed phenomena. They hope that these models will be generally, though not necessarily universally, applicable. They study particular systems in the hope that these systems are not in all respects, or in their major aspects, unique. So at least the aspirations of ecologists are not different from those of other scientists.

Ecologists, however, face problems which make their task extremely difficult, and at times apparently insurmountable. Some of the character-istics of the field of ecology are as follows. It is a young science, *as a science* probably not older than forty years, and accordingly much of it is still descriptive and necessarily so. It deals with systems which are depressingly complex, which are affected by dozens of variables—all of which may interact in, for practical purposes, an infinite number of ways. These systems must be sampled rather than censused. It is one of the few disciplines in biology in which it is not clear that removing portions of the problem to the laboratory for an experimentation is an appropriate technique. It may be that the necessary simplification that this involves removes exactly the elements from the system which deter-mine how it functions. Yet field experiments are difficult to do and usually difficult to interpret. It is the only field of biology which does not boil down to applied physics and chemistry. The great advances in molecular biology resulted from physicists looking at biological systems (such as DNA) whose basic configuration is explicable in terms of the positions of atoms. But the individual or the population is the basic unit in ecology, and it seems certain that a direct extension of physics and chemistry will not help the ecologist. Finally, there is the problem that each ecological situation is different and has a unique history; ecological systems, to use a mathematical analogy, are non-Markovian—that is, a knowledge of the *past* and present is necessary to predict the future. Ecology, unlike a great deal of physics, is both time-dependent and locale-dependent. This is not a complete list of the general problems ecologists face, but it is enough to give the reader some feeling for the difficulty of the subject. Also, although none of these difficulties is unique to ecology—for example, astronomers also find it difficult to do meaningful manipulative laboratory experiments—combined they are an imposing array.

Ecologists, though, do have *something* to show for 40 years of work.

We shall outline some of the tentative generalizations of the kinds of problems with which ecologists have been concerned. The list will not be exhaustive, but it may give the reader some feeling for the kinds of statements ecologists think they can substantiate. We shall take one of these tentative statements and explore its meaning in detail, the qualifications which must be placed upon it, and the difficulties in thinking about and testing it. By this means we hope the reader can come to understand why there are limits on what the ecological "expert" can say. Not all ecologists would agree that the following statements are generally applicable, and those who do agree would admit that exceptions occur. However, they are the sort of rules that a large school of ecologists would hope to be rble to establish.

First, populations of most species have negative feedback processes which keep their numbers within relatively narrow limits. If the species itself does not possess such features—and even if it does—the community in which it exists through the action of predators and so on, acts to regulate its number. The statement obviously is inexact; for example, how narrow are "relatively narrow limits"? A measure of the success—or lack of success—of ecology is that in 40 years there are no more than half-a-dozen populations in which regulation has been adequately demonstrated. The basis for belief in regulation is either faith or very general observations, such as the fact that most species do not strike ecologists as being so abundant that they are pests.

Second, the laws of physics lead to derivative statements in ecology; for example, (1) that matter cycles through the ecosystem to be used again and again, and (2) that energy from the sun is trapped by plants through photosynthesis. Then, as matter moves up the food chain to herbivores and then carnivores, energy is lost at each successive conversion so that generally there is less energy and biomass in higher food levels than in lower ones. Ecologists have tried to take these given truths from physics and construct more truly ecological generalities. Thus it appears likely that there are never more than five links in any one chain of conversions from plant to top predator.

Third, it is probably true that on a given piece of the earth (provided the climate doesn't change) a "climax" ecosystem will develop which is characteristic of the particular features of that place, and that places with similar features will develop similar ecosystems if left undisturbed. Characteristically, a "succession" from rather simple and short-lived communities to more complex and more persistent communities will occur, although there may be a reduction in the complexity of the final community. We use final to mean that a characteristic community will be found there for many generations. Moreover, we might say that during the period of development disturbances of the community will result in a reduction in its complexity. Again such statements would certainly arouse the ire of some ecologists.

Finally, most ecologists would concur that complex communities are more stable than simple communities. We want to develop some implications of this statement, for it is particularly illustrative of the difficulties faced by theoretical ecologists. We shall first examine what the statement means; and second, the basis we have for believing the statement.

What is complexity and what is stability in an ecological setting? Charles Elton, who may have done more than any ecologist to impregnate our subconscious with this article of faith, embodies the idea in a very simple, practical and easily understood way. He argued* that England should maintain the hedgerows between its fields because these were complex islands in a simple agricultural sea and contained a reservoir of insect and other predators which helped to keep down pest (herbivore) populations. The idea in this simple manifestation seems quite clear. Ecologists, however, want a more precise exposition of the implications of the statement—what kind of complexity? What kind of stability?

Let us deal first with complexity, which comes in several forms. Physical complexity, by providing hiding places for prey, may increase stability. Certainly biological complexity in general is thought to lead to stability—more species or more interspecific interactions, more stability. But we may ask, "more species of what sort?", and here a variety of answers is available. Elton suggested that complex communities were stable—that is, able to resist invasion by species new to the area—by having all the "niches" filled. Thus sheer numbers of kinds of organisms in all food levels were considered the appropriate sort of complexity.

To keep the numbers of prey stable the most likely candidates are predators, so now other questions arise. Do we want more predators (individuals)? Do we want more species of predators which are very specific in the prey they eat, implying that prey are stabilized by having many species feed on them? Do we want predators which are very general and attack many prey species, so that we still have a large number of interspecific interactions but made up in a different way? The answer is not obvious, and indeed there is disagreement on it.** Furthermore, if one studies the way some predators react to changes in the numbers of their prey, their short-term responses are such as to cause *instability*. Thus only some types of biological complexity may produce stability.

Now let us turn to the question of stability. What do we mean by stability? As in the examples above, by stability we have meant numerical constancy through time; but this is by no means the only meaning,

---

*Elton, C.S., *The Ecology of Invasions by Animals and Plants*. New York: J. Wiley & Sons. 1958.

**Watt, K.E.F., "Community Stability and the Strategy of Biological Control," *Canadian Entomologist 97*: 887-895. 1965.

MacArthur, R.H., "Fluctuations of Animal Populations and a Measure of Community Stability." *Ecology 36*: 533-536. 1955.

and it has even been suggested that numerical *in*constancy is a criterion for stability.* Stability might also mean that the same species persist in the same area over long periods, showing the same sorts of interspecific interactions (community stability). Elton, as we noted above, defined resistance to invasion as part of community stability. A community or population might be considered stable because (1) it does not change in response to a great deal of environmental pressure, or (2) it changes but quickly returns to its original state when the disturbing force is removed. It is worth noting that if a population or community is observed merely not to change, we cannot tell whether this is owing to its ability to resist perturbing factors or merely to the absence of such factors.** If we want to know about the *mechanisms* which might lead to the truth of our original statement, "complexity leads to stability," all of the above points are important.

It is worth examining the kind of observations that this general statement about complexity and stability rests upon. These observations are generally crude and could be made by most intelligent laymen. Thus simple agricultural systems seem to be much more subject to outbreaks of herbivores than the surrounding countryside (when there is some surrounding countryside). Ecosystems in the tropics appear to be more stable than the simpler temperate zone, and in turn the temperate zone seems to be more stable than the Arctic; this seems to be mainly an article of faith. However, even this classical sort of evidence is questioned—for example, small mammals may actually be more unstable numerically in the United States than in the much simpler Arctic environment. † Other evidence comes from laboratory studies. If one takes small species of prey and predator—for example two single-celled animals or two small mites—and starts off cultures of the two species in the laboratory, gradually they will die; most organisms die in the laboratory.

But if one is lucky enough to have the right conditions for them and they are placed together, characteristically, their numbers fluctuate and both quickly become extinct—for example because the predators polish off the prey. "Simple" predator-prey systems tend to be unstable. There is weak evidence that if physical complexity is added (such as a place for the prey to hide in) the system may become more stable.

From these examples of the kinds of rules ecologists have tried to establish, we want to raise a question for the reader's consideration. Even if we dispense with the idea that ecologists are some sort of envi-

---

*Williams, G.C., *Adaptation and Natural Selection*. Princeton, N.J.: Princeton University Press, 1966.

**Murdoch, W.W., *Population Regulation and Population Inertia*. (In preparation.) 1970.

†Krebs, C.J., "Demographic Changes in Fluctuating Populations of *Microtus Californicus*," *Ecological Monographs 36*: 239-273. 1966.

ronmental engineers, and we pursue another analogy which would equate them to pure physicists who provide scientific rules for engineers, do the tentative rules we have outlined above provide a sound basis for action by those who would manage the environment? We believe it is self-evident that they do not.

The above conclusion seems to be implied in a quotation from the article in *Time*, which underlines the point that application of the ecologists' work is not the solution to the environmental crisis.

> Crawford S. Holling was once immersed in rather abstract research at the University of British Columbia—mathematical models of the relationships between predators and their prey. "Three years ago, I got stark terrified at what was going on in the world and gave it up." Now he heads the university's interdepartmental studies of land and water use, which involve agriculture, economics, forestry, geography and regional planning. "What got me started on this," says Holling, "was the profound and striking similarities between ecological systems and the activities of man: between predators and land speculators; between animal-population growth and economic growth; between plant dispersal and the diffusion of people, ideas and money."

The "rather abstract research" was ecology, and Holling's testimony is that it would not provide a solution. Yet by and large it is ecologists who are concerned, and probably it is ecologists who have the most to say on—and the best understanding of—the problem.

We have reached the negative conclusion that ecology as such probably cannot do what is expected of it. It cannot provide a set of ecological "rules" of the kind needed to manage the environment. However, we contend that ecologists have a great responsibility to help solve the crisis, and that the solution they offer should be based on a fundamental "ecological attitude." Ecologists' training and experience make them especially sensitive to those aspects of the environmental crisis which are fundamental. They are likely to be aware of the consequences of environmental manipulation, and—possibly most important—they are preadapted to deal with the environmental problem because their basic ecological attitude is itself the solution to the problem. Interestingly enough, the supporting data generally come not from our "abstract research" but from massive uncontrolled "experiments" done in the name of development.

These attitudes and data, plus obvious manifestations of physical laws, determine what the ecologist has to say on the problem and constitute what we might call environmental knowledge. Some examples of this knowledge follow, although this is not to be taken as an encapsulation of the ecologists' wisdom! In general it sounds like advice as trite as Polonius'.

1.   Whatever is done to the environment is likely to have repercussions in other places and at other times. Because of the characteristic problems of ecology some of the effects are *bound* to be unpredictable in practice, if not in principle. Furthermore, because of the characteristic time-dependence problem, the effects may not be measurable for at least years, and possibly for decades.

2.   If man's actions are massive enough, drastic enough, or of the right sort they will cause changes which are irreversible because the genetic material of extinct species cannot be reconstituted. Even if species are not driven to extinction, changes may occur in the ecosystem which prevent a recurrence of the successional events which reproduced the community. Such irreversible changes will almost always produce a simplification of the environment.

3.   The environment is finite; our nonrenewable resources are finite, and when the stocks run out we will have to recycle what we have used.

4.   The capacity of the environment to act as a sink for our total waste, to absorb it and recycle it so that it does not accumulate as pollution, is limited and—in many instances—it has been passed. It seems clear that when such limits are passed, fairly gross effects occur, some of which are predictable but some of which are not, and these result in quite large alternations in the background environmental conditions (global weather, ocean productivity). These changes are almost always bad because organisms have evolved and ecosystems have developed for existing conditions. We impose rates of change on the environment which are too great for biological systems to cope with.

5.   In such a finite world, under present conditions, an increasing population can only worsen matters. For a stationary population an increase in the standard of living can only mean an increase in the use of limited resources, the destruction of the environment and the choking of the environmental sinks.

There are many dangers inherent in a technological "solution." The analysis in the preceding section has implications for the ecologist and indicates how he should spend his energy. There are two ways of attacking the environmental crisis. The first approach is the traditional one, technology. The second approach is to reverse the trends which got us into the crisis and to alter the structure of our society so that we establish an equilibrium between human population and the capacities of the environment. We do not claim that these two approaches are necessarily mutually exclusive, but we do claim that they are of doubtful compatibility unless a hierarchy is set up between them—and we claim that the ecologist has a duty to devote his energies to the second approach.

There are three main dangers inherent in a technological approach to the environmental crisis. The first is to the environment in the short term, the second is to ecologists, and the third concerns the general public attitude and is a danger to the environment in the long term.

Our basic premise is that a technological complex—the society and its structures and machinery—possesses mainly *positive* feedback mechanisms, especially when it is organized as a consumer-stimulating, corporate capitalism. Technology, by its nature, is a system for manufacturing the need for more technology. (This is just as true of technological solutions to the deleterious effects of technology as it is of technological solutions to problems—such as mineral exploration—which clearly require technological solutions.) When this is combined with an economic system whose major goal is growth,* the result is a society in which conspicuous production of garbage is the highest social virtue. If this premise is correct then it *a priori* becomes unlikely that we can solve our present problems using technology. As an example, we might consider nuclear power plants as a "clean" alternative to which we can increasingly turn. But nuclear power plants inevitably produce radioactive waste, this problem will grow at an enormous rate, and we are not competent to handle it safely.** In addition, a whole new set of problems arises when all of these plants produce thermal pollution. Thus technology merely substitutes one sort of pollution for another.

There is a more subtle danger inherent in the technological approach. The car, it must be agreed, is by and large a blight upon the landscape. It might be thought that ecologists should concern themselves with encouraging the development of technology to cut down emission of pollutants from the internal combustion engine. The dangers in such developments are: first, they give the public the impression that something is being done about the problem, and that they can therefore confidently await its solution. Nothing significant can be done in this way since in any case the number of cars is increasing so that the total smog problem will not diminish. Furthermore, tinkering with the juggernaut of technology is essentially equivalent to oiling its wheels, because the very act of making minor alterations to placate the public in fact allows its general development to proceed unhindered, with a concomitant increase in the remaining environmental problems it causes. This tinkering is what sociologists have called a "pseudo-event."† That is, activities go on which give the *appearance* of tackling the problem; they

*Galbraith, J.K., *The New Industrial State*. Boston: Houghton Mifflin, 1967.

Wallis, W.A., "United States Growth: What, Why, How." In: *The Goal of Economic Growth*, edited by E.S. Phelps. New York: Norton. Rev. Ed., 1969.

**Hubbert, M.K., "Energy Resources." In: *Resources and Man*, edited by P. Cloud. San Francisco: W.H. Freeman, 1969.

Commoner, B., "The Myth of Omnipotence," *Environment* 11(2): 8-13. 1969.

†Boorstin, D.J., *The Image; or, What Happened to the American Dream*. New York: Atheneum, 1961.

will not solve it but merely serve to remove public pressure for a solution. Second, the above also distracts the ecologist from his real job and makes his work more difficult. As a general rule, it is the ecologist's job to oppose growth and "progress," and he cannot set about convincing the public of the correctness of this position if in the meantime he is putting his shoulder behind the wheel of technology. The danger to the ecologist, we think, is quite clear. The political power system has a long tradition of buying off its critics;* and the ecologist is liable to wind up perennially compromising his position thereby merely slowing down slightly, or redirecting, the onslaught of technology.

The pressures on the ecologist to provide "tinkering" solutions will be quite strong. Pleas for a change of values, for a change to a nongrowth, equilibrium economy are very simple and clearly naive. The government, used to sophistication from its "experts," can be expected to take such simple advice with a certain indignation. Furthermore, ecologists themselves are painfully aware of the immaturity and nonsophistication of their science and generally take every opportunity to cover up this reality with a cloud of obfuscating pseudo-sophistication. They delight in turning prosaic facts and ideas into seemingly esoteric concepts and jargon, and where possible they embroider the structure with mathematics and the language of cybernetics and systems analysis—sometimes useful but frequently merely confusing. Such sophistication is easily come by in suggesting technological solutions, and the temptation is therefore to propose these.

Finally, there is always the danger that in becoming a consultant "expert" the ecologist will aim his sights at the wrong target. The history of the consultative expert in Washington is that he is called in to make alterations in the model already decided upon by the policymakers. Indeed, this is almost inevitable because their respective jobs are defined in this way. It would be interesting to know what proportion of scientific advice has ever produced a change in ends rather than in means. We suspect it is infinitesimal. But the ecologist ought not to concern himself with less than a change; he must change the model.

We should point out that we are not *against*, for example, substituting a steam-driven car for a gas-driven car. And there are people around who will work on this problem. Our contention is that the ecologist has bigger fish to fry. By changing public attitudes he can do something much more fundamental. In addition, by changing these attitudes he may even make it easier to force the introduction of "cleaner" technology as this also is largely a *political* decision. This certainly seems to be so in the example we chose of the steam-driven car.**

*Lasch, C., *The Agony of the American Left*. New York: Knopf, 1969.
**A series of articles and letters in *Science*; for example see, Vol *161*: 27-29 (5 July, 1968); Vol *163*: 370-374, (24 Jan., 1969); Vol *164*: 55 (4 April 1969).

It should be clear by now that we do not believe that the ecologist has something new to say. His task is to inculcate basic ecological attitudes in the government and in the people. The population must come, very soon, to appreciate simple but basic ecological notions: a finite world cannot support or withstand a continually expanding population and technology; there are limits to the capacity of environmental sinks; ecosystems are sets of interacting entities and there is no "treatment" which does not have "side effects." We cannot continually simplify systems and expect them to be stable, and when they do become unstable there is a tendency for instability to increase with time. Each child should grow up knowing and understanding his place in the environment and the possible consequences of his interactions with it. On the basis of such education, the ecologist must convince the population that the only solution to the problem of growth is not to grow. This applies to population and, unless the population is declining, to "standard of living." It should be clear by now anyway that "standard of living" probably is starting to have an inverse relationship with quality of life. An increase in the GNP must be construed as disastrous.from the ecological point of view. (The case of underdeveloped countries, of course, is different.)

We do not minimize the difficulties in changing the main driving force in American (and other peoples') lives. The ecologists' point of view indeed should be, to quote a cliche-in-the-making, subversive. We would contend that it has to be subversive or it will become merely subservient. Such a change in values and structure will have profound consequences. For example, economists, with a few notable exceptions,* do not seem to have given any thought to the possibility or desirability of a stationary economy. Businessmen, and most economists, think that growth is good; stagnation or regression is bad. Can an equilibrium be set up with the environment in a system with this philosophy? The problem of converting to non-growth is present in socialist countries also; but we must ask if corporate capitalism, by its nature, can accommodate such a major change and still retain its major features. By contrast, if there are any ecological laws, we believe the ecologists' viewpoint about the inevitability of an equilibrium between man and the environment is such a law.

We would now like to modify some points of detail of our earlier general statements. Especially after the necessary basic changes are put in motion, there *are* things ecologists as "experts" can do; some of them are sophisticated and others may even be, in a very broad sense, technological. Certainly, determining what the "optimum" U.S. population is

---

*Boulding, K.E., "The Economics of the Coming Spaceship Earth." *In: Environmental Quality in a Growing Economy*, edited by H. Jarrett. Johns Hopkins Press, 1966.

Mishan, E.J., "The Costs of Economic Growth." *In: The Goal of Economic Growth*, edited by E.S. Phelps. New York: Norton. Rev. Ed., 1969.

will require sophisticated techniques. Ecologists, willy-nilly, will have to take a central role in advising on the management of the environment, and already they are beginning to do this. The characteristics of ecology here determine that this advice, in order to be good, will be made somewhat more sophisticated to fit particular cases. Thus, good management will depend on rather long-term studies of *particular* areas, since ecological situations are both time-dependent and locale-dependent. These two features also ensure that there will be a sizeable lag-time between posing the question and receiving the ecological advice, and a major job of the ecologists will be to make the existence of such lags known to policymakers. Ecologists sometimes will have to apply technology. For example, integrated pest control (that is, basically biological control with occasional small-scale use of pesticides) will surely replace chemical control, and integrated pest control can be considered biological technology. In this area there is promise that sophisticated computer modeling techniques applied to strategies of pest control may help us design better techniques.

We have previously underemphasized these aspects of the ecologists' role, because to become caught up with them to the exclusion of much more fundamental change is to misunderstand the issues. The banning of DDT, for example, would no doubt be a laudable victory in the war to save the environment, but it would be disastrous to mistake such a largely symbolic victory for winning the war.

William W. Murdoch received his B.Sc. degree in Zoology from the University of Glasgow, Scotland, and his doctorate from the University of Oxford, England. He held a Nature Conservancy Scholarship award from 1960 to 1963. In 1963 he came to the United States, where he was, until 1965, Research Associate and Instructor at the University of Michigan. Since that time he has been a member of the faculty at the University of California, Santa Barbara, where currently he is Associate Professor of Biology.

Dr. Murdoch is the author of a number of scientific articles in the field of population ecology. Most recently he edited a book of original chapters entitled *Environment: a Source Book on Resources, Pollution and Society*, soon to be published by Sinauer Associates.

Joseph H. Connell is Professor of Zoology at the University of California, Santa Barbara, where he has been a member of the faculty since 1956. From 1955 to 1956 he was Research Associate in Biology at the Woods Hole Oceanographic Institution in Massachusetts. In his field of population biology, Dr. Connell's special interests are in the species diversity of tropical communities, especially rain forests and coral reefs; and the population ecology of marine intertidal organisms, particularly predation, competition, spatial distribution and territoriality.

Dr. Connell received his B.S. in Meteorology (1946) from the University of Chicago, his M.A. in Zoology (1953) from the University of California, Berkeley, and his Ph.D. in Zoology (1956) from the University of Glasgow, Scotland. His awards include the John Simon Guggenheim Memorial Fellowship (1962-1963), and the Mercer award (1963) of the Ecological Society of America. Dr. Connell is the author of several scientific articles on the predator-prey systems in marine intertidal regions.

CHAPTER 4

Federal Policy and the Ecological Crisis

William O. Douglas

> *Can an agency — no matter how high-minded and capable — live with [radiation protection standards] under the tremendous pressures from utility officials, manufacturers, engineers and designers that are in this business to get rich? As insurance against the day when it cannot do so, who will be the keeper of ecology?*

> *You can't make it. You can't buy it. And when its' gone, it's gone forever.* — Chief Buffalo Tiger

Ecology has become the victim not only of oil companies and timber interests but of administrative agencies. And unless the role of government, operating through its agencies, becomes more ecologically conscious, our environment will continue to deteriorate.

No administrative agency has undertaken, on its own initiative, a revolutionary function. Some agencies have been created to perform what some have thought to be revolutionary roles. But being creatures of the legislature with goals to achieve and generalized standards to guide them, they are not innovators; they indeed are like missiles which follow their designated trajectories, even though the target has been moved, or in other respects has become illusory.

Fifty years ago there was a passionate desire to convert water power into hydroelectric projects. I remember Senator George Norris of Nebraska—grandfather of the Federal Power Commission—speaking of the waters of the Potomac rolling to the ocean largely unused. They presented opportunities to create electric power and take burdens off the backs of men. And so the Federal Power Commission (FPC) (41 Stat. 1063) was created and assigned the mission of investigating and collecting data concerning the undeveloped "water resources of any region" and of issuing licenses for dams for hydroelectric purposes. The standard to be applied by the Commission was not more specific than the "public interest."

The Corps of Engineers (55 Stat. 787) was necessarily involved because some dams involved the navigable capacity of navigable rivers and sanction of the Corps was required.

Large issues as to whether the dams should be built by the United States, as are those on the Columbia, or built by licensees from the private sector were subsidiary matters. But whoever built and operated the dams, the mandate was clear: dams should be built and underdeveloped water resources should be "developed."

The Corps had a parallel function relating to flood control in navigable streams, an authority construed to include upstream control of non-navigable tributaries.

And in later years dating from 1954 the Soil Conservation Commission was given broad powers over watersheds in the interest of flood control. (68 Stat. 666.)

The Bureau of Reclamation (BOR) came into the act much earlier with control over water courses for purposes of irrigation. TVA (48 Stat. 58) is one of the newcomers.

The result of the operation of these four federal agencies has been catastrophic in the ecological sense, measured by the impact on our water courses.

Dams almost without number have been built—some highly useful, some marginal, some white elephants. The need for power has been on the increase; and though dams were built for flood control by the Corps or for irrigation by BOR, they usually have a multiple purpose.

For the building of these dams we have paid a large ecological price. The reservoir of a dam obliterates the river. The dams of Arkansas destroyed fine bass streams because the silting of the reservoir covers up the gravel bars needed for spawning, and trash fish take over. River courses commonly teem with life from deer to fox to coyotes. A dam destroys that complex community and it also wipes out rich and often exotic botanical riches. A dam and its reservoir may attract motorboats. But canoeing in white waters of the river is gone forever. The drawdown of dams often creates stinking mudholes ugly to look at, discomforting to be near, and of no known use to man. If the Corps has its way and builds the Benjamin Franklin dam near Hanford, Washington on the Columbia, the last spawning ground of the fall run chinook will be destroyed which make up from one-fourth to one-third of our entire chinook fall run.

The Tennessee Valley Authority (TVA) is presently trying to build Tellico Dam on the Little T—not for power and not for flood control, but to create industrial sites that have a waterway for transportation—at a time when it has hundreds of industrial sites still unused. That dam will inundate some of the richest farm lands in Tennessee and put under murky water forever some invaluable historic riches—and destroy the best trout stream the southeast knows. Is the so-called "development" worth the ecological damage?

Some of the agencies are probably motivated more by Parkinson's Law than by either the "development" disease or by commercial pressures. Engineers (staff engineers, that is) must do something; and those trained to build dams naturally feel compelled to build more and more of them. That often explains the white elephants that are constructed.

Far more serious than dams are the channelizing of rivers—by the Corps and by the Stabilization and Conservation Corps (SCC).

Channelization means clearing out with bulldozers the entire river bottom and then dredging a new channel. Usually the soil banks are sprayed frequently with herbicides so that no new river bottom will take over. The "experts" say that with channelizing and with dams the flow and overflow of a river can be better managed against the contingencies of floods. Those who want to see some of the damage that is done can visit Trinity River outside Ft. Worth, Texas, and see what a new and heavier torrent of water flowing through the channel can do to downstream sections of the creek bed that run through private property. Those who would be interested in seeing a river *before* and *after* channelization should go to the Sangamon River above Decatur, Illinois (the so-called Oakley Reservoir Project of the Corps) and see the gentle, purling, serpentine Sangamon in 90 miles of its journey lined with hardwoods, laced with foot trails and providing water for good bass fishing and occasional excellent canoeing. The shaded river bottom is by the way the only escape from the flat, sun-drenched land filled with corn and soy beans running to the horizon. Channelizing the Sangamon will destroy that sanctuary and make it sterile in terms of fauna and flora, where it is now extremely fertile.

The agencies I mention have no ecological standards. The phrase the "public interest" as used in these Acts has no necessary ecological bent; and it is doubtful if administrators with ecological insight and understanding are consciously chosen for the task.

When for example the FPC recommends that a federal authority, rather than a private licensee, build and operate a dam, the responsibility shifts to Congress. Every project of the Corps is an individualized one showing costs and benefits, reduced to dollar forms. The costs are construction and operating costs—not social costs as a result of a disastrous impact on the ecology of the area. So far as I know, no brochure of the Corps on a river project has ever attempted to evaluate the loss of the flora and fauna community as a result of the dam, let alone the value of a free-flowing river from the viewpoint of aesthetics, recreation, or otherwise. Yet if ecological values are to be respected, these costs are real costs in any true cost-benefit formula.

When the Corps is ready on a river project it presents the matter to the Congress. So theoretically ecological considerations can come into focus. Pressure groups of outraged citizens often seek to put in a plea for an understanding of the ecology of the problem. More and more members of Congress have an awareness of these aspects of the argument; and the scientist is often called in as an adviser. But it cannot be said that ecological factors are truly weighed in the legislative balance against all other factors.

The truth is that 50 years ago when harnessing the water resources of the nation became a burning political issue, ecology was somewhere else. Rivers, open spaces, white waters, bottom lands seemed in endless supply. We would have plenty left when all the dams needed were built.

There is now a growing feeling either that ecological standards should be written into the laws governing our disposition of the water resources of our rivers or that an outside federal authority, expert in ecology, have the authority to put a stop order against any such project that is deemed disastrous or even unwise from an ecological viewpoint.

Beyond those problems are larger dimensions. Water resources are critical; and by 2020 AD it is estimated that national demand for water will have increased 400%. This means much more than dam building and channelizing of water for flood control. It means basic revisions of the detailed management of the earth. Take, for example, the Potomac Basin. It experiences annually all the abuses to land of which man is capable. There is little state or federal property involved, mostly private. Government so far has tried to persuade farmers, builders, loggers, and the like to adopt sane conservation measures when they touch the land. The critical question being asked is whether to meet our future water needs government must get into the business of dictating what private owners may or may not do to their top soil.

While ecological factors are not very articulate when we deal with water resources, they are very much in the forefront in the field of nuclear energy.

The more one reads the more he is impressed with what "we do not know" about the limits to which we as a people should restrict population exposure to radiation. The voluminous Report of the Joint Committee in 1960 entitled "Selected Materials on Radiation Protection and Standards" is highly revealing and shows a contrariety of expert opinion. Every nuclear power plant releases some radioactive wastes into the atmosphere and into the adjoining river. It is perhaps safest to start from the premise of Dr. Russell Morgan, radiologist in chief, Johns Hopkins University when he states:

> Since it is prudent to assume there is no threshold value below which genetic and/or somatic damage may be avoided, it follows there is a large philosophical element in the development of all radiation protection standards. Radiation protection standards should be based on concepts that increased dosage brings increased risks, which in turn, call for increasing stringent controls.

Can that ecological standard be maintained at the operating level in the nuclear energy field? Can an agency—no matter how high-minded and capable—live with that standard under the tremendous pressures from utility officials, manufacturers, engineers and designers that are in this business to get rich? As insurance against the day when it cannot do so, who will be the keeper of ecology?

The peaceful use of atomic energy presents new and startling ecological questions. One need not be any kind of an expert to have positive views on whether he would like to live downwind or downstream from a nearby nuclear power plant.

The words "cheap atomic power" swept the nation about ten years ago, creating waves of excitement. Each year the Atomic Energy Commission (AEC) seemed to increase its optimistic forecast: By 1968, 2.8 million kilowatts in operation; by the mid-1970s, 73 millions; by 1980 about 170 millions. If the plants average 1 million kilowatts each, there would then be 170 plants. In the Pacific Northwest it is estimated there will be 15 new million-kilowatt nuclear power plants in the next decade.

At the present we are only on the threshold. As this is being written there are 13 commercial nuclear power plants in operation in nine states and 48 others under construction. Those who read the literature will find conflict among the so-called experts. There is no conflict as to the nature and danger of lethal doses of radioactive materials. The great differences are in the zones of "possible" accidents or "probable" accidents.

The states are now very much in the picture, often opposing the AEC. Some states are now applying more stringent standards than the AEC; and courts will shortly face the issue whether state standards must be consistent with federal standards; or, if there is dual control, when is there preemption?

The licensees—potential and actual—under the AEC law are active in the picture and they have their experts. The manufacturers are making themselves felt; and they have their experts. And Congress has its Joint Committee on Atomic Energy (JCAE); and it is a weighty agency in its own right.

In March 1957, the AEC made a report respecting the likelihood of accidents in the operation of nuclear plants and if so the extent of the damage. The report states:

> The portion of the study dealing with consequences of theoretical accidents started with the assumption of a typical power reactor, of 500,000 kilowatts thermal power, in a characteristic power reactor location. Accidents were postulated to occur after 180 days of operation, when essentially full fission product inventories had been built up.
>
> Three types of accidents which could cause serious public damages were assumed. Pessimistic (higher hazard) values were chosen for numerical estimates of many of the uncertain factors influencing the final magnitude of the estimated damages. It is believed that these theoretical estimates are

greater than the damage which would actually occur even in the unlikely event of such accidents.

For the three types of assumed accidents, the theoretical estimates indicated that personal damage might range from a lower limit of none injured or killed to an upper limit, in the worst case, of about 3,400 killed and about 43,000 injured. Theoretical property damages ranged from a lower limit of about one-half million dollars to an upper limit in the worst case of about seven-billion dollars. This latter figure is largely due to assumed contamination of land with fission products.

Under adverse combinations of the conditions considered, it was estimated that people could be killed at distances up to 15 miles, and injured at distances of about 45 miles. Land contamination could extend for greater distances.

In the large majority of theoretical reactor accidents considered, the total assumed losses would not exceed a few hundred million dollars.

On the basis of this report, Congress amended the AEC Act limiting public liability for reactor accidents. By that amendment the utilities or licensees are limitedly liable pursuant to AEC regulations which specify the nature and amount of private insurance that is available. The United States indemnifies the people suffering damages up to $500 million. So in case of an accident causing $560 million the utilities are responsible up to $83 million, the United States, $477 million. In case of a seven-billion dollar disaster about six and a half billion are put in the category of national disaster.

The AEC, like other federal agencies, is composed of honest, capable, dedicated men. But the history of regulatory agencies shows that in time their measure of the "public interest" is that which is good for the industry being regulated. In time they become industry-regulated-oriented. The prospect of this happening in the nuclear energy field is serious.

The cries for "development" are always great. The shortage of power promises to remain acute. Licensees want to make money. Manufacturers are not venal; but they make mistakes. Moreover, safety costs money; and those who make or approve design will always be under great pressure to cut costs.

In this connection the prescription and maintenance of safety standards on the disposal of radioactive wastes produced by the industry are critical. This ranges from (1) the normal operating discharge of radioactive materials into the atmosphere and water courses by nuclear plants* to (2) the production, transport and reprocessing of high-level radioac-

---

*See AEC decision Docket No. 50-286, Indian Point Nuclear Generating Unit 3 which allows 44,000 curies a day in radioactive effluent from one nuclear energy site.

tive materials. The latter entails the nature and design of the containers for this radioactive material to the carrying of these containers many miles to reprocessing plants.

The field fairly bristles with legal problems. One already mentioned is the clash between state pollution agencies and the AEC. Another concerns thermal pollution of an entire water course by reason of the large volume of water needed in the cooling process. The AEC has long maintained that under the Act it has no authority to regulate thermal pollution. And so the chorus of voices increases at the havoc that may be caused and the great ecological damage that may be suffered when a whole waterway changes its temperature from 50°F to 90°F.

The tremendous power exercised by the AEC is coupled with a tendency to suppress facts concerning the amount of radioactive wastes in the air. If I live in Duluth how do I know how safe it is to plant a vegetable garden? If I live downwind from a proposed nuclear energy plant, how can I find out (1) how radioactive is the present air (2) and how much more so will it be when the new plant is operating?

Beyond this problem is an alleged conflict of interest in the functions of the AEC. As stated by David E. Lilienthal,* former Chairman

> The AEC, as a general promoter of atomic power, must also decide the quasi-judicial issue of whether a license is issued. With a world of goodwill and integrity and technical competence on the part of the AEC, how well is the public protected by this dual and conflicting role?

The momentum of any agency is to promote the device whose control is entrusted to it. Promotion of nuclear energy may well involve cutting corners, resolving doubts in favor of the industry and against the public, and overlooking defects or weaknesses. Does this mean that the AEC prime function (development) and its second function (licensing) be separated?**

More mundane aspects of ecology appear in much of the work of the Forest Service and Bureau of Land Management (BLM). Overcutting,

---

*Lilienthal, David E., *Change, Hope, and the Bomb*. Princeton, N. J.: Princeton University Press, 1963. pp. 137-138.

**In Reorganization Plan No. 3 of 1970 (submitted to Congress July 9, 1970), President Nixon endeavored to bring all environmental protection responsibilities under a single authority, the Environmental Protection Agency. Since the plan coordinated all radiation responsibilities vested in other agencies (such as HEW), it was hoped that EPA would take over the radiation responsibilities exercised by the AEC. However, the AEC was successful in protecting its prerogatives. As things stand now, EPA has authority to regulate radiation from consumer products such as, for example, emissions from defective color television sets or microwave ovens; radiation as used in medicine; and occupational exposures to radiation for persons working in facilities not under the jurisdiction of the AEC. It also sets standards for levels of radiation in the general environment, but the AEC retains sole responsibility to set permissable radiation levels within facilities under its jurisdiction and, more important, emission levels from these facilities.

inadequate protection of watersheds, overgrazing by sheep or cattle are part of the problem. But I now refer specifically to the authority of the Forest Service and Bureau of Land Management to use sprays to kill off brush or trees deemed inimical by stockmen. If these agencies have that power, it is hidden in broad, generalized grants of authority. If the Congress ever had the purpose of including ecological consideration in the grant of authority, it expressed no opinion on the suitability of herbicides *vis-a-vis* the environment but left *carte blanche* to the agencies the decision whether to use them and if so under what conditions. These agencies have no central plots where the [impact of] herbicides on the flora of an area is studied. They proceed on the basis of trial and error, ecological decisions being made by faceless people in the south wing of the seventh floor.

The same is largely true of poisons used by these same two agencies and by the Fish and Wildlife Service to kill off or reduce the population of particular predators. The so-called experts who administer these poisons doubtless exercise an ecological judgment. But it may be truly controlled by budget considerations—which is the cheapest way to eradicate coyotes, by trappers or by poisons? If the latter, what poison?

Predator control turns on availability of funds rather than a showing of actual need. Parkinson's Law operates to induce trappers and poisoners to trap or to poison for trapping's sake or for poison's sake and to keep the bureaucracy flourishing, though the need may be slight.

We know each year more about the danger of pesticides. The toxic effect of DDT on birds and on fish in the Atlantic is now well known.

Those who have traveled the silent forests where the infamous 1080 (sodium fluoracetate) has been used have an idea of the long chain of casualties suffered when any carrion eater takes a bite of the animal that in turn took a bite of the stricken coyote, and so on. The animal that is the target is killed and so are scavengers, including birds, that feed on its carcass. This explains the virtual disappearance of the coyote in areas where he does no possible damage to man. Badgers, bears, fox raccoons, skunks, opossums, eagles, hawks, owls, and outlaws are also the victims. This is the explanation of the near extinction of the black-footed ferret which preys on prairie dogs. Some California condors—another vanishing species—have died the same way. The last grizzly bears in the arid southwestern part of the continent are now threatened by the same weapon.

We take a heavy annual toll of predators and rodents in the name of protecting crops and livestock. (See Table 1.)

These totals reflect only federal activities. No one knows what the over-all figure would be if killings by private interests and by local governmental agencies were added.

Rodent control uses mostly 1080 mixed with grain. The federal government in 1963 poisoned 260,000 acres of federal land and 1,100,200 acres of private and state land.

Table 1
Some of the Predators Killed in Control Programs

	1963	1964	1968
Bear	842	711	440
Lynx and bobcat	20,780	20,918	9,351
Coyote	89,653	97,096	69,390
Mountain Lion	294	323	152
Wolf	2,779	2,641	—

What we have done by law and are still doing in Texas to eliminate the golden eagle is appalling. The golden eagle migrates from Alaska, the Pacific West, and the mountain regions to Central Mexico and West Texas. But the golden eagle population is thinly spread over vast areas, each breeding pair occupying a territory from 25 to 100 square miles in which various nests are used in rotation.

Eagles living in Mexico and West Texas do not migrate, as they have a permanent food supply. Farther north the golden eagle depends on prey species that may hibernate in the winter. Most northern golden eagles start south in the fall when their food supply declines. It is this migrant population that is the larger part of the eagle population in West Texas. When they were killed in what became a notorious "winter shoot-off," the national census drastically dropped. The "winter shoot-off" became possible when the ranchers in 1937 got Austin officials to take the golden eagle from the list of birds protected by Texas law.

And so thousands of golden eagles were shot from airplanes in West Texas, one pilot alone killing 1,200 in one year.

The Congress in 1940 took steps to protect the bald eagle (54 Stat. 250). In 1962 the Congress undertook to protect the golden eagle as well (76 Stat. 1246). The statute provides:

> Whenever, after investigation, the Secretary of the Interior shall determine that the taking of the bald eagle or golden eagle is "necessary" for "the protection of wild life or of agricultural or other interests in any particular locality, he may authorize the taking of such eagles pursuant to regulations which he is hereby authorized to prescribe: *Provided*, That on request of the Governor of any State, the Secretary of the Interior shall authorize the taking of golden eagles for the purpose of seasonally protecting domesticated flocks and herds in such State, in accordance with regulations established under the provisions of this section, in such part or parts of such State and for such periods as the Secretary determines to be necessary to protect such interests.

By regulations the Secretary banned the taking of golden eagles "by poison or from aircraft," though he allowed their taking under permit "by firearms, traps, or other suitable means." (50 C.F.R. § 11.4).

Permits were issued by Secretary Udall as shown in Table 2:

Table 2.

Year issued	Control Period
1963	January 10, 1963-April 30, 1963
1963	December 16, 1963-April 30, 1964
1964	December 15, 1964-June 15, 1965
1965	December 15, 1965-June 15, 1966
1966	January 16, 1966-June 15, 1967
1967	December 20, 1967-April 30, 1968
1968	December 20, 1968-April 30, 1969

Since the young hatch in March and are out of the nest by early June, the foregoing periods cover the entire nesting period of the golden eagle.

The authorization to take golden eagles without permit had been extended by former Secretary Hickel to thirty-three counties in Texas for 1968–1969.

The Audubon Society made a detailed report on the matter, saying: "The slaughter of eagles and other predators is the ultimate phase in an attempt to harvest the last sheep and goat crop in a dying land."

Dr. Barton Warnock of Sul Ross College, Alpine, Texas, made the same ecological emphasis: "We know that West Texas land is too heavily pounded by sheep and goats. If an eagle takes a lamb or a kid it is protecting the land by helping restore the balance." He added, "Should eagles or any other predator for that matter reduce any rancher's sheep corp by half, most likely he still would be overstocked."

Many issues of vital concern to naturalists and conservationists rest in the uncontrolled discretion of a bureaucracy. TVA decides because of low costs that Appalachia should be dug up and ruined forever in the cause of strip mining. The BLM in spite of public outcry continues to fence the public out of public lands, making hunters and fishermen proceed at their peril, not knowing when they are on public or private lands. The Bureau of Public Roads under the hammer of chambers of commerce responds to state pressures to put a highway clear through a national forest. The Bureau of Public Roads is one of the agencies most destructive of wilderness values. It is efficient; it is politically minded; it is politically organized; it is very powerful in the nation's capital. It can bulldoze, pave, and tear up the country until most of our sacred precincts are gone. The Bureau of Public Roads, like the Corps, has a large degree of autonomy. Its plans implicate local political organizations, each of which has its contractors. A road building program for an area such as Appalachia promises to feed local political machines when the planning should be at a higher level.

Our federal policies are frequently conflicting. We spent millions acquiring the Everglades—a swamp-type national park in Florida whose very existence depends on the flow of sweet water. We now spend more millions in drawing down the sweet water of the Everglades for other interests, jeopardizing the very existence of the park.

At the federal level agencies often compete, using conflicting standards. Thus the Department of Agriculture encourages the drainage of potholes in our north central wetlands so that farmers can plant crops which in turn they can receive compensation for not planting. Opposed is the Fish and Wildlife Service with its program of preserving and enhancing the breeding grounds of ducks and geese.

The ecological problems vary from agency to agency. The ecological problems are exposed in some laws and entrusted to agency solution. In others they are ignored. In still others they are blatantly challenged in forms of vandalism that is all the more vicious because it is official.

The minimum requirement at the federal level is an Office of Conservation in the White House so that the Chief Executive may have expert ecological advice on the myriad of matters with which federal agencies deal.

From: *CQ*, January 30, 1970, p. 289

>   January 29 the President named the three members of the newly created Council on Environmental Quality. Under Secretary of the Interior Russell E. Train, former head of the Conservation Foundation, will serve as chairman. The two other members named are Robert Cahn, a Pulitizer Prize-winning reporter on resources and the environment for the *Christian Science Monitor*, and Gordon J. F. MacDonald, vice-chancellor for research and graduate affairs at the University of California at Santa Barbara.

Beyond that are political battles to be waged on ecological issues with the hope that Congress—and state legislatures—will act promptly and decisively to make sure that life on this continent does not succumb to a sickness unto death. Whether the ecologists can win the public mind over the powerful lobbies that want to convert even sunsets into dollars is an unknown.

There is a proposal to entrust to ecologists the ultimate voice in resolving these life and death issues. That could be done (1) by a constitutional amendment, taking some years, or (2) by legislative action of an Environmental Council with instant power to enter stop orders on ecological grounds against any federal agency.

The problem is acute as emphasized in the recent report of the Secretary General of the United Nations on the projected environmental conference authorized by the General Assembly for 1972.

Chief Buffalo Tiger of the Seminoles who lives near the Tamiami

Trail in the Everglades is not an ecologist, but he hàs knowledge of the problem:

> It has happened to Indians year after year; progress wasting the hunting grounds.

> Indians used to have good life here; clean air, clean water, plenty of food.

> We used to see two or three raccoons on every hummock, a lot of otters, turtles, alligators in every pond.

> Now even the snakes are scarce. The fish and turtles are going. It's hard to make a living in the Glades.

As respects the despoiling of the Everglades, Buffalo Tiger said: "You can't make it. You can't buy it. And when its gone, it's gone forever."

The same intuitive insight is in the words of Carl Sandburg in *The Sandburg Range*:

> There is an eagle in me and a mockingbird . . . and the eagle flies among the Rocky Mountains of my dreams and fights among the Sierra crags of what I want . . . and the mockingbird warbles in the early forenoon before the dew is gone, warbles in the underbrush of my Chattanoogas of hope, gushes over the blue Ozark foothills of my wishes—and I got the eagle and the mockingbird from the wilderness.

When *William O. Douglas* was appointed to the United States Supreme Court by President Roosevelt on April 17, 1939, he was the youngest (41) appointee in 125 years. During his years on the bench he has earned an international reputation as one of America's outstanding liberal jurists. Before becoming a member of the Supreme Court, Justice Douglas held professorships at Columbia Law School and the Yale University Law School. He is a graduate of Whitman College, Washington, and the Columbia University Law School in New York City.

The conservation of wilderness resources has long been a special field of interest to Justice Douglas. Among his many books are: *The Right of the People* (1958), *America Challenged* (1960), *My Wilderness—The Pacific West* (1960), *Democracy's Manifesto* (1962), *Freedom of the Mind* (1963), *The Anatomy of Liberty* (1963), and *A Wilderness Bill of Rights* (1966). In addition, he is a contributor to various legal periodicals. Justice Douglas is a Fellow of the Royal Geographical Society, London, and a member of the Board of Directors, The Fund for the Republic, Inc.

CHAPTER 5

Beware the Technological Experts

John W. Gofman
Arthur R. Tamplin

> *What we* do *know tells us that the present permissible*
> *radiation pollution levels are a travesty of public health.*
> *What we* don't *know concerning the genetic effects of*
> *radiation suggests a monumental tragedy.*

A material introduced into our environment may represent a serious biological hazard for two reasons. It may represent a hazard (1) because of what we know, and (2) because of what we don't know about the material. Our knowledge can guide us, but we must be constrained by our ignorance. For essentially every material introduced into the environment, our ignorance pales our knowledge. We know more about the biological effects of radiation than of any other environmental pollutant. What we *do* know tells us that the present permissible radiation pollution levels are a travesty of public health. What we *don't* know concerning the genetic effects of radiation suggests a monumental tragedy. At long last we should heed Claude Bernard, "In ignorance, refrain."

Radiation Hazards

Irrational (Present) and Rational (Hoped-for) Management of Aspects of the Environmental Crisis

The presumption is widely made that in some mysterious way a rational approach will be forthcoming that will enable man and his ecosystem to survive environmental degradation. With much fanfare a stern glance is cast upon a particular smokestack, the latrine output at West Point, or an oil slick in the Gulf of Mexico. As a result of the fanfare, it is assumed that a new day of attention to our environmental integrity has dawned when, in fact, all the irrational approaches of the past are tenaciously defended and all suggestions of a rational future approach are slandered and ridiculed as the work of conservationist "kooks."

For those who do not understand that our environmental crisis is other than accidental, it is essential to review the nature of technological application of scientific discovery. It is within this general approach to development of technology that all the difficulties lie and the future catastrophes are carefully prepared. Nothing is left to chance. Our approach of the past and, unfortunately, of the present virtually ensures disastrous ultimate results.

So similar are the various technologies in generating their respective parts of the environmental crisis that almost any of them could be chosen for illustrative purposes. All such technologies can be regarded as "polluters" of man himself, of the ecosystems which support him, or of the inanimate environment.

Radiation exposure and radioactive contamination of the biosphere make up the problem of radiation pollution. An argument could be made for radiation pollution as deserving the Number 1 position among environmental hazards; as good an argument can be made that other approaches to extermination of life on this planet preempt this leading position because we won't be around long enough to suffer from radiation destruction. What is important about radiation pollution is that its study exemplifies all the errors of the past and the formidable obstacles to reasonable action in the future. The history of the automobile would serve as well, but since our area is atomic energy, we shall attempt to outline the general principles which concern us by using radiation pollution as a framework of specifics. Elements of the problem are discussed under the six following categories.

The Atomic Age Dawns

Roentgen's discovery of the X ray in 1895 and Becquerel's discovery of natural radioactivity in 1896 are key anchor points in the field of radiation pollution. Any attempt to gainsay the remarkable nature of the phenomena involved would be foolish. Clearly, these discoveries brought a new dimension to chemistry, physics, and biology—a dimension best described in two terms: (1) The packet of energy involved is massive compared with the previously familiar infra-red, visible, and ultra-violet packets of light energy. (2) Atoms, or more precisely nuclei, undergo transformations where the energy release *per* transformation is as much as, or more than, a million times the release accompanying *chemical* transformations, for example, in the oxidation of carbon to carbon dioxide.

Man's curiosity and his quest for an ostensibly better life inevitably lead to a rapid exploration of the possibilities for exploitation of the new discoveries—in medicine, in industry, in warfare, and in the furtherance of scientific investigation itself. It would be difficult indeed to find a scientific discovery or technical development where this sequence of events does not occur. Roentgen's X rays and the Curies' radium were very rapidly introduced into medical diagnosis and medical therapy. While, in retrospect, one may look with horror at the rashness of man in exploring his new technology, history teaches us that such rashness has not shown any signs of abating. In medicine, the frustration over the inability to cope with unsolved major diseases at any point in time is understandable, even if it leaves one shaking his head at the readiness with which almost *anything* new is tried. Here we see the introduction of the cult of worship of technical progress, of the scientific method, with the undying confidence that science and technology are progress; more progress is up, and up is (by definition) good.

There is always the assurance that the new technology *must* be wonderful, that any appearance otherwise is but an indication that we have not yet learned how best to extract the full measure of wonders the technology or new scientific discovery has to offer. And even before this *is* learned, if indeed it be there to be learned, the "good is up" philosophy leads to a rapid expansion of the science and its technology. In the field associated with radiation and radioactivity some of the important mileposts are the discovery of the nucleus of the atom, the neutron, artificial radioactivity, nuclear fission, and the self-sustaining nuclear fission chain reaction. The net result of all these epochal advances is that nuclear energy release is possible in fantastic quantities, and radioactive substances are available in massive abundance, packageable with a richness of varieties that put the famous Heinz-57 to shame. Since "good is up," in this field it is believed that the "good" must indeed be super-marvelous, for the "up" is certainly astronomical.

In the early stages of an area of science or science plus its technological offshoot, the practitioners are not many and, rash as they may be, their small numbers preclude, in general, global consequences of stupidity and poor judgment. But, as with the technology itself, the practitioners themselves believe progress means more practitioners, more centers dedicated to the particular science and technology, more applications of the technology. This inevitably breeds more "progress" in the technology, the requirement for more practitioners, et cetera, in an ever-upward spiral.

Somewhere in this chain of developments, the science or technology becomes consequential enough to require a public relations agency, a lobby for the activities. For small science or small technology, the professional associations, the business associations subserve these functions. In the field of radiation, radioactivity, and atomic energy, the phenomenon comes to require the same Madison Avenue approach applied by Detroit with the automobile. The time for the Super-promotion has arrived; it is too late for the small professional or business association.

The Super-promoter Takes Over the New Technology

The Super-promotional approach can arise in either the private or the public sector, depending upon circumstances; the final result is the same. In either case a *super-agency* is the fundamental requirement.

For the automobile, the super-agency was achieved in the form of "Detroit," a triumvirate of corporations, aided by Madison Avenue, and dedicated to bringing the supreme benefits of the automobile way of life to every hamlet of the land. So exquisite was this new way of life that the ultimate goal of success in life became the achievement of the two-car garage, the total obliteration of the landscape by the freeway, and the final denial even of maintaining the physiological integrity of man (and his family) in the absolute requirement to devote his resources to the care and feeding of the automobile. Surely the super-agency, "Detroit," did its job of ensuring the widest possible spread of this stunning technology unflinchingly and faithfully.

In the field of radiation and atomic energy, the peculiar circumstance that a military application itself led to major parts of the scientific-technological spiral has dictated the establishment of the requisite pro-motional super-agency in the public sector rather than in the private sector. This was achieved, by act of Congress, in the establishment of the Atomic Energy Commission (AEC), with the specific mission (in the nonmilitary area) of bringing the benefits of the atom to the populace, with (what has become an afterthought) due consideration of safety and health of the public. When "Detroit" exercised its role of promoter of the automobile, the issue of public health and safety was hardly noticed (until recently, *very* late in the game). The question of *regulation* in relation to promotion hardly existed. In the establishment of the AEC due notice was given to the *regulation* part of the story because of the appreciated power of the technology itself, but one of the fundamental errors of history was made by the Congress in assigning to one super-agency the roles of both promoter and regulator. Obvious as the conflict between the promotional and regulatory activities of the AEC has become, there is vigorous denial by the AEC and by the super-promotional Joint Committee on Atomic Energy (JCAE) that *any* conflict in these roles exists. Unctuous statements of self-praise abound from both the AEC and JCAE, and sycophants are available within science and industry in abundance to confirm the mythology of a consistency in promotion and regulation. We shall return to this conflict later.

As a super-agency dedicated to the widest spread of the new technology, the AEC has truly rivaled Detroit, figuratively and literally, unfortunately. The AEC has several product lines, as has Detroit, and it is vigorous in merchandising all of them at once. Among these products are nuclear energy itself, available for conversion to heat and electricity; atomic and hydrogen bombs; radiation sources; and radioactive substances by the carload. One criterion alone signals successful execution of its mission for the AEC: namely, an ever-rising curve of output and distribution of all its product lines.

Nuclear electricity is heralded as cheap, even though its true expense is hidden by fantastic overt and covert tax-supported subsidies and the necessity to kill uranium miners with lung cancer to achieve such "cheapness." Nuclear electricity is "pollution-free" because its poisonous radioactive by-products are not optically *visible* as are the belching columns of smoke from poorly-designed fossil-fuel generating plants.

Nuclear bombs, unpopular when exploded directly upon the population, still need merchandising. According to the AEC, there are relatively few human needs that cannot be fulfilled with an appropriately designed nuclear explosive, atomic or hydrogen. Canals can be dug, harbors created, mountain cuts made, rivers diverted—all with nuclear explosives, provided one doesn't look too deeply at the residual radioactivity spewed and strewn about the earth. And we can, thanks to the foresight and hard work of the AEC promoter, have all the harbors, canals, et cetera, that we want, because nuclear bombs are now cheap! We are going to have stimulated yields of underground natural gas, oil from shale, and metals from ore deposits—all by exploding underground nuclear bombs. Never mind the radioactivity associated with the gas, the oil, or the metals recovered. Indeed, recently a major promise for ridding the earth of garbage has come from promoters of nuclear explosives, via the technique of creating huge underground garbage pits by explosion of large nuclear bombs. And all these fabulous benefits are upon us—we can have thousands of such explosions per year in the immediate future.

With characteristic frugality, the AEC promises us it will stay economical and, like Armour's pig, use everything but the squeal. Its refuse by-products are being made available in the form of radiation sources of great intensity, and radioactive substances to assist every scientific, industrial, and medical endeavor. The curve of shipments of such radiation sources and radioactive substances rises annually, signaling great success in the frugal exploitation of by-products of the technology. That a probably large, and largely unknown, fraction of the radiation and the radioactivity finds its way by numerous routes into the biosphere, including man, in a cumulative fashion, is almost wholly overlooked for the recipients and users are "licensed."

So, the Super-promoter of Atomic Technology, the Atomic Energy Commission, fulfills with splendor its mission of champion of the technology. The Atomic Energy Commission is assisted by liberal use of tax dollars for massive public "education."

Hazardous By-products of the Technology

The environmental crisis is upon us for a very simple reason; few technologies are free of side effects. Only recently have we come to realize that *numbers* of our technologies have side effects of such potential magnitude as to be capable of obliteration of massive segments, if not all, of our ecosystems. Atomic energy can be regarded as an archetype. Indeed, it is especially significant to consider radiation as a prime example because the lethal side effects were apparent shortly after Roentgen's discovery of X rays. Yet despite this, there is not a shred of evidence that this long-standing knowledge has made the development of atomic energy technology one iota more rational than those with far more obscure side effects. How does it become possible for the side effects to remain so poorly appreciated?

We must recall that technology is wondrous and that "good is up." Thoroughly imbued with these items of "knowledge," the superagency gallant knights feel deeply their responsibility to reassure the public that we *can* have the exquisite benefits and solve the side effects problem by devoted research and development. Chairman Seaborg of the AEC is expert in the reassurance approach to coping with side effects. "We must learn to live with the atom wisely," he intones, "and this we are doing well." Other equally prominent atomic energy proponents tell us that "undue alarm can stifle progress" and "progress has brought us all the fruits of civilization we have." Professor Edward Teller recently sought to allay the concern about radioactivity voiced by Senator Mike Gravel with the reassurance that our methods of getting radioactivity out of people are improving all the time. If we expose people to radioactivity, we'll clean them up, Professor Teller is ready to assure us.

At some stages in a technology, such as atomic energy, the platitudinous reassurance approach suffices to quiet public fears, especially if the platitudes are repeated on a regular schedule. The difficulty for the technology arises, however, from the fact that the side effects *are* real, and they fail to melt away under platitudinous reassurance; that is, the side effects are obvious and cannot forever escape public awareness. Precisely this has happened in atomic energy, much to the consternation of the AEC, which now encounters a nuisance in the path of its mission to bring society the blissful benefits of the atom.

Thus, as a result of medical and industrial uses of radiation and atom bombings, a large number of humans have been exposed to radiation. If the side effects, as for example cancer or leukemia, had been immediate, the AEC would have been seriously embarrassed many years ago. For reasons not yet understood, such side effects of radiation exposure as cancer or leukemia require 5 to 20 years to manifest themselves. Side effects such as irreversible damage to the genes will only appear in future generations of the individual radiated. This delay in manifestation of side effects has proved enormously useful to the AEC, for it has been able to carry on activities involving radiation of humans for many years, and each year point out that humans are still alive (at least until the 5 to 20 years had elapsed and the leukemias and cancer became obvious to everyone).

Recently we have estimated from the medical evidence already on hand from persons who had been radiated as described above, that the currently allowable radiation dose used as an AEC guideline, would, if everyone in the USA received such a dose, result in 32,000 extra deaths annually from cancer plus leukemia alone. This number can only be increased *materially* if the future genetic malformations and deaths are added in and if the less well-defined other radiation effects, such as life-shortening, are taken into account. So 32,000 extra cancer plus leukemia deaths annually are, in essence, a minimum estimate of damage to humans. The magnitude of this damage itself is apparent when we realize that there are some 320,000 spontaneous deaths from cancer plus leukemia annually. So-called "allowable" radiation, purported to be "safe" radiation, will therefore add *one* extra cancer death for every *ten* that would otherwise occur. This would have to be regarded as one of the major public health disasters of all time. And at the extreme is the possibility that genetic and chromosomal defects induced by this so-called "allowable" dose of radiation may be enough to obliterate life on earth in a finite number of generations.

The False Concept of a "Tolerance" Dose of Radioactive Poison

The reader will certainly ask how the promoter, the AEC in this case, ever arrived at a certain radiation dose as "tolerable" or "permissible." This goes to the very heart of the problem all technology promoters face when side effects rear their ugly heads. The AEC, like other super-agency promoters of technology, have as a prime objective the growth ad infinitum of their technology. The first step is a total denial that side effects are related to the technology, especially where the individuals exposed to noxious by-products, such as radioactivity, don't drop over dead immediately upon exposure. Denial of these delayed effects buys the promoter time for unbridled exploitation and rape.

But a second line of defense is soon needed. This is the so-called "tolerance" or "allowable" dose approach used by the AEC and all other technology promoters. For most poisons, the fraction of people killed by the poison goes up with increasing dose. It becomes obvious, therefore, that lethal effects are perceived early in groups of persons who are massively exposed, say, to radioactivity as a poison. Suppose 100 persons are exposed to a particular dose of radioactivity and that 50 of them die of cancer. The promoter of atomic energy technology then comes up with an *ingenious* pronouncement—that particular dose of radioactivity must be above the "tolerance" or "allowable" dose.

So, a new "tolerance" dose is set somewhere below this amount of radioactivity exposure, even though not one bit of evidence exists that *any* dose will be tolerated without producing cancer or leukemia. But for a promoter of technology, like the AEC, taking away the concept of a "tolerance" dose is far worse than taking candy from a child. For, so long as a "tolerance" or "allowable" dose can be reset at some lower value, more time is available for the technology to proceed before it becomes obvious to everyone that even at the lower dose, grossly unacceptable numbers of humans are being killed by cancer and leukemia. It's just that it takes longer to prove that 5 out of 100 people are being killed than it takes to prove that 50 out of 100 are being killed. The promoter thus buys more time for exploitation.

Actually, any poison that kills *one* extra human out of *10,000* is a major public health disaster. So between the proof that 50 out of 100 are being killed by a radioactive poison and the proof that one out of 10,000 is being killed, there are innumerable opportunities to keep setting the "allowable" dose successively lower and, hence, buying more and more time. During all this, the atomic technology can flourish, tens of thousands of humans can be murdered annually—all legally—under the deception entitled "within the allowable tolerance." And, as a bonus, the hereditary gene pool of the human race is irreversibly damaged, to say nothing of irreversible contamination of the planet.

As the experience from human exposure to radiation and experimental animal exposure has accumulated, it has become painfully clear that no evidence exists, or has ever existed, that suggests there is *any safe tolerance dose* of radiation.

How then did we get into this irrational box of the "tolerance" dose for a variety of technologically produced poisons? We did so because of the role of super-agencies as promoters of technology. One doesn't have to consider the AEC, which is a prime example, as a group of evil men dedicated to the destruction of human life, even though their actions may lead to precisely this result. By casting them in the dual role of promoter and regulator, we forced their actions to be evil even when their intentions may have been good. One has only to observe the reflex decerebration manifested by the AEC or the JCAE when the words death or cancer from radiation exposure are mentioned to appreciate how inappropriate this dual role is. Criticism of such decerebration is no more indicated than is criticism of reflex behavior of a dog conditioned to salivate at the ringing of a bell. And this leads us to consideration of more rational approaches to development of technologies like atomic energy.

The Super-promoter and His Experts vs. the Public

Our endeavor above has been to show that promotion of technology by a super-agency, such as the AEC, is an all-consuming affair, leaving little or no room for an ability to contemplate the consequences to humans of the technology. The humans who desire not to be victimized by the rashness of the entrepreneurial approach are required, in what has to be the acme of injustice, to *prove* that the technology has harmed or will harm them. The AEC is *not* required to prove that their emission of radioactive poison *is* safe. Far from it! An individual who wishes to raise a question about the safety of his exposure to radioactive poisons must use his own personal resources of funds for legal counsel and legal procedure. Arrayed against him is the entire Solicitor General's office of the U.S. Government and the vast resources of the AEC to "purchase" testimony from hangers-on whose resources of research funds and livelihood derive directly from the AEC. And if this lop-sided array were not sufficient, the added insult is provided by the judiciary branch of government. The judiciary, as recent decisions indicate, operates on the presumption that the government would surely not set "tolerance" standards that are unsafe for the individual. Why and how this strange optimism on the part of the judiciary has arisen escapes understanding, but it is a fact of existence. In summary then, an individual can be denied life, liberty, and the pursuit of happiness by a governmental super-agency, and if he complains of the abrogation of his constitutional rights, he is likely to find major branches of government, with fantastic resources, arrayed against him with the purpose of denying him those rights.

For years now we have been hearing of the inordinately good record of the atomic energy industry with respect to safety and freedom from fatal accidents. (Just because the AEC Commissioners are making such assertions, we should not automatically assume that the assertions are false.) However, even minor probing is sufficient to reveal that the assertion of a good safety record is not only false, it is absurd. It turns out that the record is "good" because it is so *defined*. Defining a record as good is achieved by the simple expedient of vigorously denying culpability for deaths that are obviously the direct result of the exposure to radiation of the industrial employee.

Let us consider the case of an atomic energy industry worker who received, over a 20-year period, the amount of radiation labeled as "tolerance." This he is legally allowed to receive. Our estimates, in good general accord with those of the respected International Commission on Radiological Protection, would indicate that after a latency period of 5 years or so, two out of every three cancers occurring in such workers are the *direct* result of the occupational exposure. So if we observe 100 cases of cancer or leukemia in such workers, it is certain that approximately 67 of them are occupational. If the workers request compensation, the claim is summarily denied on the grounds that the exposure was within "tolerance" limits. By the remarkable expedient of defining a radiation dose which triples the cancer rate as "tolerance," the atomic energy industry absolves itself of responsibility. Thus, by simple definition, the atomic energy industry has an excellent safety record, even if it produces thousands of fatal cases of cancer and leukemia.

A Rational Future: Zero Tolerance for Pollutants

Clearly, a new approach is needed. Technology sings its self-praises of the wondrous benefits it is conferring, or is about to confer, upon the unwitting population. When pressed, a technological super-agency, such as AEC, adds to its repertoire of lullabies about benefits a new tune, entitled "The Benefits Outweigh the Risks." As sung by the AEC Commissioners, the ditty is meaningless and, of course, they have no intention that it shall be otherwise. But within these words is the germ of an idea that can be the basis of a rational approach to technology and its associated poisonous by-products. Society may indeed require the benefits a new or existing technology has to offer. Further, society may find itself in a position where it is willing to accept certain grave risks in exchange for receipt of the benefits. It can be said, without any fear of contradiction, that society has never been given the opportunity to do so for three major reasons: (1) the *benefits* have always been vaguely described, at best; (2) the *risks* have been denied, minimized, or lied about; and (3) no weighting of benefits against risks by society has even been approached, because self-styled "expert" groups have made any such (dubious) calculations of this sort *for* society.

The flagrant disregard for the primacy of human health in such matters is beautifully illustrated in the 1967 Hearings before the JCAE on the subject of the outrageously high lung cancer death rate being caused in uranium miners by exposure to radioactivity in the mines. We shall quote directly from The Federal Radiation Council Report No. 8, entitled "Guidance for the Control of Radiation Hazards in Uranium Mining" (September 1967). Direct quote:

> *Factors Related to the Evaluation of Benefit and Control Capabilities*
>
> Available information on benefits to be derived from the mining of uranium, difficulties encountered in reducing radon daughter concentrations from previous levels to current levels, and the additional difficulties that can be anticipated if further reduction in radon daughter concentrations are required has also been reviewed. The findings of immediate interest are as follows: (1) Uranium is currently the basic fuel needed for the development of nuclear energy, and all projections point to an increasingly important role for nuclear energy in meeting national electric power requirements. (2) Uranium mining is an important economic asset to the States in which the ore is mined. In addition to the value of the ore, mining provides important opportunities for employment. It is estimated that the work force will vary between 2000 and 5000 men in the next decade.

Stripped of euphemisms, the Federal Radiation Council staff appears to be saying it would be tragic to have nuclear fuel, uranium, cost a little more just to keep uranium miners from an epidemic rate of lung cancer. After all, the country needs electric power. Further, it helps the economy of the mining states, and if we make the mines safe, business might decline.

The final result in this magnanimous weighing of benefits versus risks occurred when the redoubtable Atomic Energy Commission recently awarded a $200,000 contract to the Arthur D. Little firm "to study the *economic impact* on the uranium mining industry" if they were forced to clean up the mines to a point where the lung cancer epidemic among miners might be mitigated somewhat.

This all needs total restructuring with the following integral elements:

First, total abolition of the concept of a "tolerance" or "acceptable" dose of a poison such as radioactive material. This is required forthwith.

Second, establishment of a broadly representative commission, including scientific and nonscientific membership, to receive requests from promoters like the AEC for new technological programs that will expose large segments of the public to a poison such as radioactivity.

Third, all requests for such technological programs, for example, nuclear reactors to produce electric power for society, must be submitted to the commission, including an honest and detailed "benefit versus risk" calculation. Such a calculation would obviously be incomplete without: (1) detailed estimates of benefits to be derived in the form of numbers of lives to be saved annually, or quantitative estimates of the improvement of life quality; (2) detailed estimates of risks to be experienced in the form of number of deaths from cancer, leukemia, and other diseases, including genetic damage and ecosystem damage; and (3) supportive evidence to back up (1) and (2).

Fourth, the Commission, in possession of the detailed benefit-risk (lives saved versus lives lost) calculations, then would announce public hearings concerning the proposed atomic technology (nuclear reactors for electric power), and invite the broadest participation by all segments of the public in such hearings and an evaluation of the goodness of the evidence submitted.

Finally, the public, either by referendum or via Congress, can vote the allowance of delivery of an amount of radiation specified, and accept the known risk in deaths to be produced thereby. This it will do in exchange for receipt of the benefits it has been convinced it will receive from said technology: nuclear reactors for electricity.

In addition, it is inevitable that hazards or benefits may, with further experience, turn out to be grossly at variance with those presented for original consideration and vote. Therefore, a mechanism must remain open for reconsideration of the issue on a current basis. The new evidence can very well result in a reversal of the public decision. Certain corollaries are important: (1) Either government or the private sector generates proposals for new technologies. There is no dearth of *advocacy* of technology to be foisted upon the public; witness some of the hare-brained nuclear bomb proposals of the AEC. (2) There is a *gross* dearth of responsible constructive criticism of new proposed technologies. In such establishments as the Atomic Energy Commission, even mild internal opposition to any proposed technology is met with apoplexy on the part of Commissioners, slander by AEC staff members, and overt and covert reprisals and reprisal threats. Such phenomena are indeed successful in virtually guaranteeing that a possible adverse environmental impact of a proposed technology is almost never heard of *within* the AEC establishment. Therefore, it is imperative that reprisal-free, independent groups be created with the explicit purpose of finding out all the deleterious possible impacts of the proposed technology. These groups must have ready access to rapid publication methods and dissemination of their findings openly to scientific and lay public alike. Funding of such groups by the promoter agency is an absolute disaster. Participation of promoter agencies in *any* regulatory role should be unthinkable. (3) Local groups (state, city level) must to the fullest extent possible retain the final prerogative of refusing the proposed technology with its concomitant death risks even when nationally it has been accepted. (4) The result of all these procedural changes should establish for the future that human hunting licenses for such promoters as the AEC are summarily abolished. The burden of proof of safety should unequivocally be placed upon the promoter, not upon the victim of the promoter.

It can be confidently predicted that such technology promoters as the AEC and the JCAE will ridicule, obstruct, and in every conceivable way attempt to discredit these proposals. Indeed, the true merit of the proposals will run in direct proportion to the outcry from the promotional agencies. It will, of course, be stated that the proposed method for the introduction of new technologies will be cumbersome, will take too much time and effort. We would counter with the suggestion that society can not afford to *avoid* undertaking this responsibility.

Sanity can hardly be described as an outstanding feature of our approach so far to technologies like atomic energy. But there can be no fundamentally evil aspect to a sane approach to environmental questions. We shouldn't knock a rational approach without ever having tried it.

Radiation and the Induction of Cancer and Leukemia

There exists by now a large body of detailed information concerning the injurious (including lethal) effects of ionizing radiations (alpha particles, beta particles, neutrons, X rays, and gamma rays) on numerous animal species studied in the laboratory, as well as upon man. Indeed, the experimental animal data have long provided sufficient evidence concerning radiation hazards to have led to a rational approach for consideration of the hazard to man. Unfortunately, because of the promotional aspects of atomic energy development, it is required that we first see the human corpses before any such hazard is acknowledged. In no other field do we proceed in such an incredible manner. Indeed in the food additive field, human use is barred if cancer production is demonstrated experimentally in *any* species. This represents elementary common sense as a public health approach. Such common sense has at no time characterized the approach in the field of radiation.

Thus in assessing radiation hazard for man, a massive deception has been foisted upon the unwitting public. With respect to causation of leukemia and cancer the story is truly appalling. Those involved in promoting this technology have demanded, and still demand, in evaluating hazards for man, that direct observation of corpses from each and every type of leukemia and cancer be required. This has led and *continues* to lead to a colossal underestimation of the radiation hazard for man, in a manner important to describe here.

Two large population samples of humans having received radiation were available for observation, unfortunately. The first group was represented by the survivors of the Hiroshima-Nagasaki atomic bombing; the second by some 14,000 persons in Great Britain who had received X radiation in the course of treatment of the painful arthritis-like disease known as ankylosing spondylitis. As the years passed for both of these groups, it became apparent that leukemia was occurring with an inordinately high frequency both in the the atom-bombed Japanese survivors and in the X-irradiated British subjects. The data were clear-cut; no one in the world medical community has the slightest doubt that the excess cases of leukemia are caused by the radiation, nor about the quantitative aspects of the relation.

What happened? Instead of an immediate realization that what we knew all too well from experimental animals was occurring in humans, precisely the wrong conclusion was drawn. The animal data had shown that leukemia and essentially all other forms of cancer were inducible by radiation. The leukemia occurrences in humans should have led to the expectation that all other cancers, inducible in experimental animals, were *going* to occur in humans. Instead, the radiation experts heaved a big sigh of relief to learn that *only* leukemia *appeared* to be a consequence of radiation. Further they (the experts) were perfectly happy to base any projections of radiation hazard upon this occurrence of leukemia, with total neglect of everything they knew from a vast body of experimental animal evidence about the many forms of cancer inducible by radiation over and above leukemia. So far as they were concerned only leukemia had thus far occurred in humans, and until and unless human corpses were produced as a result of other cancers, they refused to consider other cancers as a potential result of radiation.

This grave error is a monument to human opportunism, stupidity and indifference. Fortunately the error is being slowly understood, and (hopefully) rectified. It turns out that the only reason why other cancers didn't show up in the British and Japanese radiated persons is that such cancers take a little longer to become manifest than does leukemia. It has long been known, from experimental studies, that cancer and leukemia are not immediate effects of radiation, but are, rather, delayed effects. This time period between the radiation insult and the clinical manifestation of the cancer has been designated as a *latent period*. What goes on during such a latent period remains a biological mystery; we simply know it exists. In humans, for reasons unknown, the latent period for leukemia is approximately 5 years. For other forms of cancer in humans the latent period is longer, even 15 years or more for some cancers. And this is the simple reason that leukemia *appeared* to be the only late effect of radiation. The radiation experts knew all about this latency phenomenon. They knew full well that other forms of cancer might take longer to appear. But because of the promotional philosophy, they refused to acknowledge this, for to do so meant making the radiation hazard look more serious. However, time *did* pass, and steadily numerous forms of cancer became clearly evident as late radiation effects both in the British and the Japanese. As each new form of cancer was proved, beyond any reasonable doubt, to have been caused by the radiation, the experts grudgingly acknowledged such cancers as additional human hazards from radiation. They then revised their numbers to account for these additional cancers, but steadfastly refused to consider any other cancers as possible effects of radiation.

Last year we were endeavoring to make some reasonable sense out of the steadily accumulating evidence of additional forms of cancer being added as those proved to be produced by radiation of humans. We came to the realization that almost all the major forms of human cancer were by then already known to be produced by ionizing radiation. For all intents and purposes it would hardly matter whether the remaining rarer, or minor, forms of cancer could also be produced by radiation. So it became possible to state a primary principle, or "law" of radiation production of cancer in humans.

That principle or law states

All forms of human cancer are, in all probability, induced by ionizing radiation.

Following this important generalization, the very next question which arises concerns the quantitative aspects of the problem. How many cancers or leukemias are produced per unit amount of radiation received by the humans? Before presenting the evidence concerning this, a definition is required for the amount of radiation received by tissues and organs of the body. The *rad* is the commonly used unit of radiation energy absorbed. Whenever a tissue absorbs 100 ergs of energy per gram of tissue, we define this as representing *one* rad of radiation delivered. It doesn't matter whether the radiation is from alpha particles, beta parti cles, X rays, gamma rays, or any other possible sources of ionizing radiation. The rad is simply defined as the tissue absorption of 100 ergs of energy per gram. It is true that some radiations will penetrate more than others, and hence *delivery* of the radiation may be hard to achieve if there is intervening material for nonpenetrating radiation. But the rad unit does not address itself to the issue of penetrability; rather it deals only with amount of energy absorbed in biological tissue.

So, our question can be restated now as "How many cancers or leukemias per rad of radiation delivered to humans?" Examination of the data accumulated from many sources, including the atom-bombed Nagasaki-Hiroshima survivors, the X-irradiated British subjects with spondylitis, the neck-irradiated children in the USA, the fluoroscoped tuberculous patients, led to a startling, but very simple, conclusion concerning cancer plus leukemia induction in humans by radiation.

The conclusion is that a particular dose of ionizing radiation increases *all* cancers and leukemia approximately in proportion to the spontaneous incidence of those particular cancers or leukemia. This important generalization can best be appreciated by reference to specific cancers and leukemias.

Leukemia occurs spontaneously in approximately a hundred out of a million people each year in the USA. The accumulated data from several of the worldwide studies show that radiation produces each year about two cases of leukemia per million people who have been exposed to a total dose of one rad of radiation to their bodies. This means that a 2% increase in leukemia incidence each year is the result of having received this one rad of radiation.

When the results for other forms of cancer in humans are examined, it is found that one rad results in approximately a 2% increase in the incidence of many forms of human cancer. Thus if a cancer is a common one, say, occurring in a thousand persons out of one million each year, then one rad will produce 2% of one thousand, or twenty, cases of that cancer each year. So the same amount of radiation (one rad) produces two extra cases of leukemia each year, but twenty extra cases of a more common cancer each year.

Thus, the *second* important generalization, or law, arrived at is the following:

All forms of cancer and leukemia are increased by ionizing radiation in direct proportion to the spontaneous occurrence of such cancers or leukemia. Best estimates at this time suggest a 2% annual increase in incidence rate for every form of human cancer and leukemia for every rad of radiation accumulated by human adults.

Whether the value of 2% increase will finally be the precisely correct one depends upon further data accumulation. What *is* of moment is that the increase is indeed very large (2%), and we can feel quite confident it is not likely to be below 1% nor above 4%.

A most serious implication becomes apparent through this generalization. Appreciation of this generalization requires an examination of the information concerning the spontaneous occurrence rate of all cancers in comparison with leukemia alone in the USA at various ages. Such data are available in the U.S. Vital Statistics, utilizing 1966 as a representative year, and are reproduced here in Table 1.

Table 1

Age Group (years)	All Cancers (except leukemia) (cases per million persons per year)	All Leukemias (cases per million persons per year)	RATIO Diverse Cancers Leukemias
Under 1 year	37.4	15.0	2.49
1- 4 years	44.1	44.1	1.00
5- 9 "	37.3	40.8	0.91
10-14 "	40.6	27.6	1.47
15-19 "	63.9	27.7	2.31
20-24 "	89.3	24.5	3.64
25-29 "	120.5	20.8	8.53
30-34 "	187.8	27.2	6.90
35-39 "	336.9	31.1	10.83
40-44 "	650.4	41.0	15.86
45-49 "	1209.1	52.9	22.86
50-54 "	2301.8	80.7	28.52
55-59 "	3786.3	132.1	28.66
60-64 "	5782.8	197.8	29.24
65-69 "	8422.9	289.6	29.08
70-74 "	10901.0	464.8	23.45
75-79 "	12982.1	586.3	22.14
80-84 "	15014.1	709.6	21.16
85+ "	17199.9	923.3	18.63

What can be *expected* if radiation insult were accumulated by groups of humans at various ages? First it is necessary to recall that a certain period of time, the latent period, will elapse before *any* cancers or leukemias will become manifest. For illustrative purposes we shall simplify the problem here by assuming all cancers and leukemias to require approximately ten years before starting to appear clinically in the radiation-exposed humans. (That some first appear earlier than ten years, and others later is secondary in *these* considerations). Once the latent period is over, cancers and leukemia continue to occur *each year* for long periods—possibly for the entire lifetime of the individual.

Thus, if a group of radiated 25- to 29-year old persons were studied ten or more years after exposure, there would be 8.53 times as many radiation-induced cancers of diverse organs as leukemias. A group of 35-to 39-year old persons would develop 10.83 times as many miscellaneous cancers as leukemias. By age 50 to 54 years, the miscellaneous radiation-induced types of cancer would be 28.66 times as frequent as the radiation-induced leukemias.

This is the real import of the second generalization above, and this is the reason we ourselves were so shocked by the implication of our observations that had led to this generalization. The radiation cancer hazard was thereby shown to be *huge* in contrast to the previous estimates—estimates that were all falsely low simply because leukemia became manifest in radiation-exposed humans *earlier* after the radiation than did the many diverse forms of cancer.

This generalization leads directly and simply into the estimation of the devastating effect upon human life if the current Federal Radiation Council Guidelines for population exposure are allowed to remain in force. These guidelines have never had any more than a "by guess and by gosh" justification. About all that ever was claimed even by the Federal Radiation Council itself was the hope that somehow the benefits to be derived from allowing humans to be irradiated to this extent would outweigh the harm that could accrue. That harm, from cancer and leukemia alone, is easily estimated from the generalizations above: (1) 1 rad increases all forms of cancer in adults by 2%; (2) federally allowable dose accumulation is 0.17 rads per year, or 5 rads from birth to age 30 years; (3) $5 \times 2 = 10$. So, accumulating 5 rads leads to a 10% increase in cancer plus leukemia occurrence; and (4) since approximately 320,000 cancers occur spontaneously each year in the USA, a 10% increase means some *32,000 extra cancers plus leukemias each year* in the USA.

In all fairness to the Federal Radiation Council it must be emphasized that they do not *advocate* giving every person the full allowable dose of radiation through peaceful atomic energy activities. Indeed, they even suggest it would be wise, from the public health point of view, to keep radiation exposures "as low as possible." It is this key phrase, "as low as possible," that must be explored. For the Federal Radiation Council, participated in and largely dominated by the AEC and the Department of Defense, really uses a *separate* criterion to guide its actions. That criterion is that the amount of radiation they will allow must consider "operational needs" as much as or more than the public health. Thus if the favorite promotional hucksterism of the AEC would result in delivery of radiation sufficient to produce 32,000 extra cancers and leukemias per year, this is known as "operational needs." And Dr. Paul Tompkins of the Federal Radiation Council has testified before Congress that "operational needs" might require raising the allowable exposure of the population *threefold*. Leaving aside euphemisms, this means the promulgation of atomic energy programs may require the annual murder of 96,000 Americans by cancer and leukemia.

The intelligent reader might be disbelieving of the possibility that a governmental agency such as the AEC would countenance programs that could result in 96,000 extra cancers plus leukemias per year. It would, indeed, be unfair to suggest that the AEC wants to commit such wholesale slaughter of humans. The mechanism operative is a bit different. First the AEC officials, including the Commissioners and the Congress proponents on the JCAE, particularly Mr. Holifield and Mr. Hosmer, all decide the peaceful atom is obviously grand. It can do no wrong. Besides, in the words of AEC Chairman Seaborg, we are learning to live with the atom wisely and well. Having decided this, many officials close their minds to any possibility that the hazard can be serious. Next, they become certain that the motivation of anyone who questions their pre-eminent wisdom is necessarily evil—indeed even treasonous. Once this step is reached, such officials lash out in a raving, maniacal orgy of irrationality at anyone so brash as to even raise a question about radiation hazards. Fortunately, their credibility has sunk to such low depths that almost no one believes anything they say concerning the health hazards of radiation. The Congress of the United States is relatively rapidly becoming educated concerning the diatribes emanating from AEC headquarters, and from their well-paid sycophants whether in Washington or spread around the country.

But the wheels move slowly in our democracy, and they have not yet moved sufficiently far to remove the hands of the AEC dynasty from the public treasury. And so long as this is not accomplished, the peaceful atom and its proponents will preserve the *license* to kill 32,000 humans annually from cancer and leukemia.

Genetic Consequences of Radiation

It is important to point out at the outset of any discussion of the genetic effects of radiation that we know the effects are harmful but we do not know how harmful. This is emphasized by the United Nations Scientific Committee on the Effects of Atomic Radiation.

> Since neither a comprehensive estimate of the genetic risk, nor an upper limit to that estimate is available, the assessment of genetic damage from main sources of radiation must still be made by means of comparative risks.

In other words, we know that ten rads of radiation are worse than one rad, but we don't know how harmful one rad is. At the same time, in the United States and elsewhere, we have a so-called permissible level of exposure. This level corresponds to that recommended by the International Commission on Radiological Protection. The public is often told that this level is safe or negligible. But consider the highly qualified aspects of this recommendation.

Because of the need for guidance in this regard, the Commission in its 1958 Recommendations suggested a provisional limit of 5 rems* per generation for the genetic dose to the whole population, from all sources additional to natural background radiation and to medical exposures. The Commission believes that this level provides reasonable latitude for the expansion of atomic energy programs in the foreseeable future. It should be emphasized that the limit may not in fact represent a proper balance between possible harm and probable benefit, because of the uncertainty in assessing the risks and the benefits that would justify the exposure.

Notice that they indicate that a major consideration was allowing a "reasonable latitude for the expansion of atomic energy programs." One wonders whether the recommendation of this group of "experts" should be accepted without question. Is the "reasonable latitude" really reasonable? Should not a much broader segment of society than this small group make this decision—a decision for all men and all time?

There are two components of the genetic effects of radiation. (1) Lethal effects that lead to death before maturity or that lead to sterility, and (2) nonlethal effects that contribute to the general pattern of illness and mortality in adult life. In the population the present pattern of illness and mortality results from a complicated (and essentially totally unknown) interplay between heriditary factors and the environment. The mechanism by which radiation would be expected to influence these patterns is by altering the genes and chromosomes that determine the hereditary factors transferred to the child.

The United Nations Scientific Committee on the Effects of Atomic Radiation states

> It is generally accepted that there is a genetic component in much, if not all, illness. This component is frequently too small to be detected; in other instances the evidence for its presence is unequivocal. Nevertheless, the role of genetic factors in the health of human populations has not in the past been considered seriously in vital and health statistics. As a consequence, data on the prevalence of hereditary diseases and defects are now largely restricted to that collected by geneticists for special purposes in limited populations from a small number of countries.
>
> An assessment of the hereditary defects and diseases with which a population is afflicted does not necessarily provide a measure of the imposed burden of suffering and hardship on the individual, the family, or society.

This can be paraphrased as "most of our information concerning genetic disorders in man relates to simple gene mutations in such rare diseases as hemophilia. This is only the top of the iceberg because *all* human disease has a genetic component."

---

*1 rad is equal to 1 rem for most of the radiations encountered.

The United Nations Committee goes on to state in a rather pedantic manner.

> In the absence of complete information about the role of balanced poly-
> morphic systems it is usually assumed that most of the genetic damage
> within populations is mutation-maintained; this avoids the risk of underes-
> timating radiation damage. Even if this assumption is incorrect, it is pos-
> sible that most new mutant alleles at loci involved in polymorphic systems
> are unconditionally harmful in contrast to those alleles which support the
> polymorphic systems in nature. In these circumstances it is important to
> know the average reduction in fitness of the heterozygote, since this value
> determines the number of generations over which a temporary increase in
> mutation rate would be felt by a population. It also determines to some
> extent the magnitude of the total damage. There is no general information
> about this value in man. In Drosophila, extensive studies have indicated
> that the average reduction in fitness of heterozygous lethals and semi-
> lethals is about 2 per cent. It would probably be larger in poor environ-
> mental conditions.

This can be paraphrased as "most human disease has a genetic component but it is not related in a simple way to a simple dominant-recessive
gene system. The major human diseases are determined by the interplay
of a large number of genes and the environment in an unknown
fashion."

Recently Dr. C. O. Carter has published conclusive evidence demonstrating a multi-gene basis for such major diseases as diabetes, ischemic
heart disease, schizophrenia, and rheumatoid arthritis. Ischemic heart
disease (coronary heart disease) kills two or more times as many Americans annually as all forms of cancer combined. The toll of schizophrenia
socially is best stated as massive.

In estimating the genetic effects of radiation the above considerations
indicate that it is essential to assume that all of the illness and mortality
patterns are a consequence of mutations in the population. By this
assumption, if the mutation frequency were doubled, these death and
disease rates would be doubled. This is the only reasonable assumption.

The United Nations Scientific Committee on the Effects of Atomic
Radiation estimates that one rad would increase the natural mutation
frequency by a factor between 1/10 and 1/100. The existing radiation
protection guidelines would allow a genetically significant dosage of five
rads. This could increase the mutation frequency and hence increase the
death and disease rates between 5% and 50%. As an upper limit then,
the radiation protection guideline dosage could increase the death and
disease rates by 50%. It is difficult to understand how the present allowable exposure of five rads in 30 years is justified *even* if the true effect
were the smaller value, that is, 5%.

As we indicated in the earlier sections of this discussion, the more
recent data on the biological effects of radiation are generally tending to
demonstrate that the original optimistic opinions of the effects were

wrong. For example, we now realize the extreme radiosensitivity of the developing fetus in utero. To a considerable extent the existing guidelines were based upon the effects of radiation on adults, and the data of Stewart and others are now demonstrating that the developing fetus is from ten to a hundred times more sensitive than the adult. In addition, the data are suggesting that leukemia is not the most sensitive form of cancer with respect to radiation, but that indeed all cancers are equally likely to be induced. Further, the data show other cancers which occur in the population more frequently than leukemia are indeed by radiation in proportion to their occurrence rate.

The early estimates of the genetic effects of radiation were based upon studies of the fruit fly (Drosophila). Unfortunately, the extension of the genetic studies to the mammal (mouse) revealed that the genetic mutation rate per unit dose of radiation was much higher than that observed in Drosophila. This certainly should be a cause for caution in extrapolation of the mouse genetic data to humans.

Finally, the data which are now coming in from biological experimentation are suggesting that the most radiosensitive portion of the biological system was overlooked in setting the original standards. This part of the biological system is represented by the chromosomes; that is, the "packages" of genes. Radiation can affect genetic material in two major ways. One way, which is the one that has been given the most attention with respect to the genetic and somatic effects of radiation, is that of producing a point mutation. By this process irradiation changes the structure or the composition of a single gene; that is, a single hereditary unit. Through this process is determined the production of a point mutation. On the other hand, it is now abundantly clear that the radiation can also affect the chromosomes. By this process the radiation is able to alter or remove from the genetic material not a single gene but a large number of genes. The developing evidence on chromosomes and the effects of radiation on chromosomes suggests that this process may represent the major mechanism through which radiation produces its damage both somatically and in a genetic way. In other words, a whole new mechanism for the potential biological effects of radiation is now evolving, a mechanism that may represent a far greater susceptibility of man than any previous mechanism proposed. What should be shocking is that only now are we *beginning* to learn about the massive disease and death-producing effects of alterations of chromosomes—a body of knowledge beginning to be accumulated *after* the experts, totally ignorant of such phenomena, had already decided on so-called "acceptable" doses of radiation.

And what does the UN Committee have to say about this new body of evidence?

> Present knowledge of dosage effects on the induction of chromosome anomalies is too scanty to predict a doubling dose. There are indications

that monkey chromosomes and, hence, perhaps those of other primates are more radiosensitive than those of mice. The Committee is of the opinion that ionizing radiation would increase the prevalence of developmental congenital malformations and of serious constitutional disorders, but no quantitative estimates can now be made.

We think it is extremely important at this juncture to point out that scientists are not omniscient. Though we have a considerable body of information at our disposal, we can never be certain that we have made all the pertinent observations that are necessary to determine the outcome of a particular series of events. We must always keep in mind that we do not necessarily have all the significant facts before us when we are asked to make recommendations as to whether something which is planned will not adversely affect man or his environment. The recent developments that occurred with thalidomide represent a useful example in this respect. As a consequence of the rather tragic results of the use of thalidomide, the drug testing procedures have now been altered. Following the thalidomide disclosure, we now find many drugs listed in the *Physicians Desk Reference* that have a pregnancy warning which was not recorded previously. In fact, as ridiculous as it may seem, drugs in the *Physicians Desk Reference* that were initially issued primarily for the treatment of nausea in early pregnancy now have a warning against their use in early pregnancy.

It would seem that we have a similar situation now with respect to the biological effects of radiation.

Subsequent to the establishment of the exposure guidelines, a whole new body of experimental data concerning the radiosensitivity of chromosomes has been evolving. Recent results reported by a group from Johns Hopkins University may demonstrate quite well the importance of the new body of data with respect to the biological effects of radiation. The Johns Hopkins data indicate that between one and two rads delivered in the first 30 weeks in utero life will produce severe genetic damage, and in this case it appears to be chromosomal damage to the fetal germ cells. As a result of this damage, 50% of the female conceptuses of women who were themselves irradiated as fetuses will be killed. This is a very startling observation, and other confirmations of this observation are necessary and highly desirable. It is an effect the magnitude of which far exceeds anything that had previously been predicted concerning the genetic effects of radiation.

One of the existing dogmas concerning the genetic effects of radiation is that only sex-linked mutations would be expected to contribute to deaths in the F-1 generation (the children born to irradiated parents). Such sex-linked lethal mutations would express themselves by the deaths of male fetuses. As a consequence of sex-linked lethal mutations, one would then expect to find the male-to-female ratio to be depressed in the live births. However, contrary to this existing dogma concerning the genetic effects of radiation, the Johns Hopkins study, rather than showing a depression in the male-to-female ratio, indicated that the male-to-female ratio increased. Not only did it increase, it doubled. In other words twice as many boy babies were born as girl babies and this is from mothers who were irradiated as fetuses at dosages in the range of one to two rads. The Federal Radiation Council Guidelines for the population-at-large would allow some 0.1 of a rad to be delivered in the first 30 weeks of in utero life. Considering the Johns Hopkins data, this could result in the deaths of some 2½% of the female conceptuses. Further, it would appear only reasonable to assume that an equal fraction of the conceptuses would be affected by the nonlethal, but nevertheless severe, life-shortening chromosomal changes. All that is suggested here is that this is most likely not an all-or-none phenomenon, that changes in the chromosomes less than lethal undoubtedly can also be expected to occur. It would not seem to be unreasonable to assume that, in addition to the 2½% of the female conceptuses that are killed, something on the order of 1% of the surviving live-born infants might have severe or significant chromosomal changes.

Considering that each year in the United States we have some four million live births, this would suggest that as many as 40,000 additional severely affected children might be born as a result of this in utero irradiation.

How serious are the genetic effects of radiation? No one knows! It is possible that exposure at the present allowable levels could result in a 5% to 50% increase in the death and disease rate, producing some 150,000 to 1,500,000 additional deaths each year for an ultimate population of 300,000,000 people. It is also possible that exposure at the present allowable dosage could result in the birth of an additional 40,000 severely affected children each year. Moreover, the evidence suggests that there would be (over and above the lethal diseases) a 5% to 50% increase in such crippling diseases as diabetes, rheumatoid arthritis, and schizophrenia. With the present radiation guidelines we shall be practicing an insidious form of sadism and genocide. With which thought this case study of the Atomic Energy Commission might fitly close.

Combating Benign Neglect: A Proposal

There are many things wrong with science in this country, but its major fault is that it has become a meaningless set of WPA projects. There are also many things wrong with technology in the country, but its major fault is that it does not respond to the needs of society. The present growing environmental crisis demonstrates that science and technology have actually begun to operate to the detriment of society in an obvious manner. Yet we find that the scientific advisor to the President is chosen because he supports the ABM development and that the President announces a new goal for the space program which is nothing more than a meaningless WPA project. The SST promises to be a disastrous WPA project. Then the President decides to cut the budget for the NIH, and no one can really argue that this cut will have any significant effect on medical science. The AEC pushes high-energy physics and builds BEV accelerators. This is the area where the money is, so young physicists go into this area. Now the JCAE is disenchanted and the young physicists are out on a limb. In reality, there is reason to believe that the BEV program is another overrated program that grew all out of proportion.

Scientists pursuing these meaningless WPA projects do not represent a direct detriment to society. They, however, do pose an indirect threat to society in that they are used to support the concept of the omniscience and omnipotence of science and technology. They offer credibility to the proposed ABM system and thereby offer thinkability to a nuclear war; they create the illusion that if we really get into trouble with our environment, science and technology will be able to rescue us and they divert the scientific manpower away from more meaningful programs.

Science in itself is not bad or good, that is why it has no ethic. Without application, science is meaningless. But most of science in this country is meant to be applied and, hence the government, hand in glove with industry, rules over science by controlling the purse strings. As a consequence, science in this country must either be irrelevant or part of some mission prescribed by government in consort with industry.

Many scientists have spoken out against the ABM system, war-related research, the SST and NASA. Many have complained about the prong priorities in mission-related research. Many have sounded the alarm concerning the impending environmental crisis. Why haven't they been more effective? One reason is that the majority of scientists are second-rate hacks who support the proposed projects, either openly or by silence. The public, therefore, assumes that the majority of the scientific community supports the programs while a few dissidents are making noise. But the major reason is that it takes money and time to fight city hall. The proponents are well organized and well funded by government and industry; not so for the opponents. Moreover, the opponents must present a much stronger case against a program than the proponents present for the program.

What Needs To Be Done

Quite obviously we need a mechanism for effectively criticizing present day science and technology, and for articulating a new set of priorities that would lead science and technology to fulfilling the needs of society. In order to accomplish this, a group of scientists have to be funded for this purpose. Moreover, it is absolutely essential that they be funded in such a manner as to be completely independent of government and industry.

The scientists who compose this group must be activists in the best sense of the word. They must interact with members of Congress and the various activists and pressure groups in the country. The association with activists, pressure groups, and with Congress can serve two purposes. First, it will aid the scientists in understanding and articulating the basic needs of society. This will aid the groups and Congress in such articulation. Second, it will give the scientists a mechanism for creating public awareness. The one essential ingredient in this interaction is that the science be unassailable. For if the technical detail of the science is not superb, the impact will be minimal.

Their immediate role must be to undermine the unwarranted public and congressional confidence in existing science and technology. They must show that science and technology are not meeting the needs of society and, in fact, are actually compounding the problems of society. But, at the same time, they should not be just destructive in their criticism. They must offer alternative programs that represent routes to the solution of the needs of society.

We would propose that, at most, only 100 scientists would be required. The entire program would thus cost less than five-million dollars a year. These scientists would work in centers. Each center would have 10 to 15 scientists. The numbers are not arbitrary; they represent a critical and limiting mass of interacting scientists within a center, and the same applies to the number of centers.

The program would start with one such center, and the number and nature of the additional centers would evolve from the initial center's study in six months to one year. The first center would be required to structure the problem; that is, to create the framework upon which the needs of society can be related to existing science and technology. By this process they would identify the major facets of the problem, and this identification would lead to the number and nature of the other centers.

This structuring and ordering of the problem has to remain open. The first cut will probably have to be modified in many of its details. At the same time, it will be the very important first step.

Moreover, this structuring cannot be done in the abstract. It must be approached as a problem-oriented project. We would suggest that this initial problem be the three faces of the GNP—gross national product, gross national power, and gross national pollution. All of these are interrelated, and the three together eventually must become self-limiting. By the year 2000 the United States population is expected to reach 300 million. An important parallel study would be to freeze the GNP at the present level and to look at the nature of technology in the year 2000 under this constraint.

It seems quite evident that science and technology have become uncoupled from our society. It makes little sense that with our GNP, we have so much poverty and unemployment. The only explanation would seem to be the recently coined process, benign neglect. The same would apply to the pending environmental crisis. This phenomenon of benign neglect permeates our society, and its net effect is the decline in the quality of life.

In short, what is needed is a group of competent scientists who would criticize any new application of science or expansion of technology. Or more succinctly, a group of scientists who would oppose the creation of new forms of garbage while advocating means of disposing of the presently accumulated garbage. It must seem that we are suggesting an end to technological progress. Quite the contrary, we are only suggesting that technology should no longer be an end unto itself, but it should be the means by which society meets its ends.

John W. Gofman is a nuclear physicist and nuclear chemist whose many scientific contributions to the nation include his work as discoverer and inventor in the atomic energy field. As an educator he has over twenty years of university teaching in the radioisotope, radiobiology field. As a researcher he has worked on Low Dose radiation, chromosomes and cancer; and as a writer he has authored approximately 130 scientific publications plus additional reports and three books. He is the co-editor of *Advances in Biological and Medical Physics*.

Dr. Gofman has been a member of the faculty at the University of California, Berkeley, since 1947, where currently he is Professor of Medical Physics; jointly, since 1947, he has been Research Associate at the Lawrence Radiation Laboratory at Berkeley and Livermore, California. Dr. Gofman received his B.A. in Chemistry from Oberlin College in 1939, his Ph.D. in Nuclear/Physical Chemistry from the University of California, Berkeley, in 1943; and his M.D. in Medicine from the University of California, San Francisco in 1946, with his Internship at the University of California Hospital, San Francisco, in 1946 and 1947.

Arthur R. Tamplin has been with the Lawrence Radiation Laboratory, Livermore, California since 1963. As a Group Leader in the Biomedical Division he has been responsible for developing an adequate state-of-the-art ability to predict the ultimate distribution within the biosphere, particularly the concentration in man, of each and every radionuclide produced in the explosion of a nuclear device. In addition to determining the concentration of the radionuclides, this program is concerned with the effects of their radiation on man. During the period June 1947 to January 1969, he was a member of the AEC's Division of Biology and Medicine Committee on Space Nuclear Systems Radiological Safety. The primary interest of this committee was the hazard of plutonium.

Dr. Tamplin is a graduate of the University of California, Berkeley, where he received his B.A. in Biochemistry, *cum laude*, in 1953, and his Ph.D. in Biophysics in 1959.

2

Thoughts Toward Survival

The authors in this section also point to numerous discouraging facts and situations, but concentrate on curative suggestions and action plans. Professor Ken Watt tries to show what a powerful tool planning could be, if it were long range as well as short range, if it considered all remotely possible elements and contingencies, if it were continually subject to review — and if it ultimately had a serious effect on decision making. Edgardo Contini proposes a deceptively simple way of eliminating smog while focussing corporate and social energies in positive directions. The method could as well be applied in almost every pollution situation. Mr. Michael Kitzmiller has had some experience framing environmental legislation, and points out a number of the difficulties involved in using the law to right environmental wrongs. He opts for an "Environmental Bill of Rights" in the Constitution and an independent federal environmental entity as the best of the current governmental ideas. Professor and Presidental Advisor Neil Jacoby argues that the changes to be made are serious ones, but that they are well within the reach of a redirected technology and a self-conscious citizenry. Dr. Alexander King lists many of the current worldwide environmental efforts, serious and faddish. He approves of what is going on, but warns that we haven't as yet admitted the depth of the problem. It is a basic question of species survival, and with the seriousness of the disease, we probably won't make it if we continue simply to treat the separate symptoms. We will need a universal awareness of the problems, and very likely new institutions and attitudes to overcome them.

CHAPTER 6

Planning—So There Will Be a Future

Kenneth E. F. Watt

> *All economic forces operate to promote and hasten annihilation; none operate against it.*
>
> *The first and most basic problem we must deal with is people's attitudes. Thinking must be changed with respect to children, property, land, agriculture, the future, and the delusion of grandeur in which we are all ensnared.*

"We Have Met the Enemy, and They Are Us"

It is all too easy, in assigning blame for the current ecological crisis, to point an accusing finger at the "government," or "big business," or other institutions. Admittedly, our institutions have real defects which contribute to the crisis, as we shall discuss later in this chapter. However, we all have a variety of erroneous beliefs which are important contributors to the problem. After all, the government is not totally unresponsive to the will of the electorate. If 90% of us were strongly opposed to air pollution, the government would have to clean up air pollution. The fact that the government and other institutions have done so little about the environment until recently is mute testament to the fact that most of us simply did not believe that it was worthwhile. In this chapter we seek to identify those particular beliefs characterizing this culture which have permitted the situation, and which must be changed rapidly if the planet is to be saved.

This is a *Now* culture. To illustrate how different we are from previous cultures, consider those civilizations which built pyramids and cathedrals. The three large pyramids in Egypt took about 20 years each to construct, at a time when man's mean life span was about 35 years. Thus the ancient Egyptians were prepared to begin a project which would take over half the lifetime of an average citizen. The cathedrals of the 11th, 12th, and 13th centuries often took several generations to complete; the great cathedral of Notre Dame in Paris took 90 years to complete, about twice the mean life span of the people who built it. Our culture does not undertake projects with this time requirement. The most ambitious project undertaken by modern America, the moon exploration, took only 12 years from conception to completion, about one-sixth the mean life span of the population.

This great stress on *Now* also shows up in a widespread unwillingness to sacrifice short-term pleasures for long-term benefits. The public has been bombarded with information strongly indicating a causal connection between smoking and respiratory mortality, yet this has had remarkably little effect on cigarette sales. Women are told that cosmetic injections of silicone into their breasts can lead to cancer, but the practice continues. How can such a population be expected to care whether there is a planet earth for their children in the year 2000, or even the year 1974?

The consequence, of course, is that the public is entirely willing to stand by, silent, while great and increasing tracts of prime farmland are converted to tract housing, with no questions about where tomorrow's food will come from. We have also been willing to watch an explosive increase in the fuel consumption per capita in the United States, with no questions being raised about where tomorrow's fuel will come from. The public stays silent while some people concerned about the future talk of food resources in the oceans, and at the same time the oceans are being so poisoned with our wastes that now even the Gulf of Mexico may die. And, of course, poisoned seas produce no food.

A much more serious problem than this preoccupation with *Now*, but linked to it, is the failure to perceive fairly obvious changes in the world and to ask questions about the relationships between different changes. One of the most striking examples of the absence of public questions concerns the relationship between smog and weather. The smog pall over the earth is clearly intensifying and spreading. It is not just research meteorologists flying planes all over the world to measure concentration of particles at 4000 feet and up who can see this; anyone who flies much on business trips cannot help but see the phenomenon. It is curious that so few questions are being raised about the obvious effect of smog in cutting down sunshine, and the increasingly noticeable deterioration of the weather that began worldwide in 1950 and which showed up so markedly in the 1969-1970 winter. This was an extremely cold winter in Russia, Germany, New York, and as far south as Raleigh, North Carolina long-standing records were broken. From September 1, 1969 to January 22, 1970 the daily mean temperature in New York City averaged over two degrees lower per day than the long-term mean for the same period. This may not seem like much, but it was enough to have marked effects on crop production. For example, in one county in California alone, farmers estimated a 5.1-million-dollar loss from losses of crops (grapes, 45%; prunes, 35%; pears, 25%) caused by the unseasonably cold weather in 1970. The 1969-1970 winter should have been an "off" year, but we had an influenza epidemic for the second year in a row, probably because of the low resistance in people brought about by the severe weather. Perhaps the reason so few people notice weather trends is that the temperature does not drop steadily from year to year, but rather drops gradually, with fluctuations about a dropping trend line.

It is curious also that so few people have grasped the significance of the views from the moon spaceship flights of the earth as a small, lonely ball in empty space. Those views told us that we live on a finite planet, and consequently there must be a limit to the amount of all goods available to us. How can we reconcile this with our avowed goals of a higher gross national product each year, and more conspicuous consumption and waste each year? Surely, it must have occurred to most people that there are limits, for example, on the availability of many resources. All the crude oil in the world will be gone in 24 to 32 years if present trends continue. Why is there so little public concern with this fact, which might well mean a return to an 1800 world of one-billion people?

A fundamental explanation for the ecological crisis is that modern communications and competition make possible a constant pattern of rising expectations in the entire human population. That is, the wants of any person anywhere are increasingly geared to the standard of living of the most affluent person anywhere. Thus everyone is made to expect that he should burn fossil fuel and nuclear fuel at an ever-increasing rate, and use minerals and wood at an ever-rising rate, *et cetera*. Indeed, the whole point of advertising is to manufacture a very high level of expectations and demands. Competition between nations makes for great inefficiency in fuel use, as with the large number of nations that operate jet service between London and New York.

People all over the world are being trained not to think in terms of a limit on supply, but rather on a constantly escalating spiral of demand. Indeed the idea is systematically promulgated that growth is good, inevitable, and there are no limits on anything.

It is remarkably difficult to counter this argument, for an interesting reason. It is extraordinarily easy to find information on benefits that accrue from growth, but it is remarkably difficult to find information on social costs of growth. For example, real estate sections of Sunday newspaper supplements extoll the merits of a move to the suburbs, but there is very little discussion about costs of taxes, congestion and smog on the freeway during the two-hour daily roundtrip downtown, or the consequences to the cultural life of the urban core from geographically splitting residences of high-wage earners from sites where they make their money. Nor do real estate developers hint that we might drive up food prices by covering the best farmland with freeways or houses in sprawling suburbia.

We are not encouraged to consider such problems, and this leaves untouched the hidden assumption that we don't need to, because the solutions will always come from someone else, somewhere else, rather than ourselves. This is a variant of the American Dream: if you don't find life pleasing here, move West. The answer is always elsewhere. This implied assumption has some rather frightening consequences. For example, there is no doubt that orange juice and other citrus products add to the quality of life in America. Yet both Florida and California are gradually replacing citrus groves by tract housing, a more profitable ("higher use") way to make use of citrus groves. Thus, each state would apparently like to get out of farming. The danger in this situation, of course, is that each state imagines that some other state has a different attitude. What if they all have the same attitude? Which state has clearly volunteered to supply us with farm products?

And We Get Worse When We Get Organized

In this section we shall point out defects in planning, and also the problems that arise in implementation of planning, even where the planning is sound. The way in which the defects have implications for various types of basic social process are also indicated. Later we shall suggest some solutions that should enable us to deal more effectively with many of our current planning problems.

The human foibles which operate against rational thinking about the future are carried into large organizations by the people who staff them. However, when large organizations make decisions about the future many additional problems arise as a result of the defects of design and functioning of organizations. This is not a new idea: C. Northcote Parkinson and John Kenneth Galbraith have already pointed out that large organizations may in fact have basic problems arising out of their mode of organization which divert their energies from their true goals. Ralph Nader in effect is conducting experiments on the ideas of Parkinson and Galbraith, and has shown that he can in fact do a better job of protecting the consumer than immense government organizations with huge budgets, or than corporations which should have been able to maintain rigid quality control on their products. Indeed, the notion that institutions with stated goals may not be able to attain those goals because of defects in the way in which they are organized and operated is one of the most important ideas circulating in the world at present. Because so many people feel that a problem is being dealt with adequately once the government has begun to work on it, it is important, in order to know how to rectify its situation, that we understand how it is that government and other large institutions can fail.

Many readers will have become amazed at the bewildering number of areas of human activity characterized by an almost total absence of any rational comprehensive planning. Bad land use policies are urbanizing our best agricultural land; our fossil petroleum is being squandered;

failure to control environmental pollutants is affecting public health, crop growth and the weather; and a lack of population policy is crushing the middle-class taxpayers. How is it that there are defects in planning in such a wide variety of problem areas? One is left with the nagging suspicion that there may be fundamental defects in the way in which planning is done in many areas, and that the phenomenon discussed by Parkinson, Galbraith and others is nearly universal. If this is so, then it is worthwhile to consider if there are any discernible common patterns in the planning defects that occur in many fields.

One of the most striking defects in almost all planning is that the only institutions or individuals sufficiently knowledgeable about the problem to do the planning are already committed to proceed with a project before planning even begins. There is no real objective consideration of all the alternatives open to the planners, because one of the most important options, namely no action at all, has been excluded from the outset.

If planning were to be conducted with complete objectivity, it would begin by considering relative costs and benefits of an array of broad strategic options, such as

1. take action number one;
2. take a variant of action number one;
3. take action number one, but defer initiation of the project for three years;
4. take action number two instead of action number one; and
5. take no action at all for the foreseeable future, and reconsider this decision in 24 months.

In fact, for reasons having to do with the structure of human institutions, option (5) above, which may be most attractive from a cost-benefit viewpoint, is rarely considered.

There has been much criticism of the military-industrial combine. A principal complaint is that there is no effective institutional check on the activities of either military suppliers or purchasers, because to make such a check would require expert knowledge which is largely classified. For this reason, purchasers and suppliers often operate cooperatively rather than by using strict competitive bidding. In fact, the same objection can be raised in almost all areas of human activity. Government highway agencies represent a community of interest with construction agencies, agriculture departments with the agricultural industries tourism departments with the tourism industry; all of these agencies represent joint constituencies with the corresponding industries, with which there is a community of interests. That is, a state highways agency can hardly be expected to recommend that the state stop building highways. The difficulty in all such cases is that there may be no agency with the power, expertise, influence, planning and analysis capability and staff to be able to recommend no action on a sound technical basis. Thus one reason our society is so growth oriented is that our institutions are all organized to promote growth and argue for its merits, even though a cursory examination of the available information by a staff with sufficient technical skill would often reveal that no action was the most economic policy.

In short, the only people or institutions who have the expertise to recommend the fifth type of strategy option on a sound technical basis typically have an overwhelming emotional commitment to one of the first four options. By default, therefore, the most important part of the decision-making process is left to senior executives and administrators who have an overwhelming bias in terms of taking some action. This means that most planning is, in effect, largely an accommodation to the philosophy of the economic benefits to be derived from growth. Land planners are hired to find out the most rational and aesthetically pleasing way of subdividing farmland for tract housing, though their studies may lead them to the conclusion that the land should not be subdivided at all. The terms of their hiring do not allow them to consider this as an available option. Real estate developers, luxury resort planners, airframe manufacturers, and road builders are scarcely reliable sources of policy decisions that real estate should *not* be developed, seashore should *not* be converted to luxury hotel complexes, supersonic transports should *not* be built, and highways should *not* be constructed.

It will be clear to many readers that just because senior executives have a great deal of money, power and influence does not mean that their judgement is invariably sound. On the contrary, there is ample historical evidence that the type of person who is oriented toward growth and development can very easily let his enthusiasm run away with his common sense. A characteristic of resort areas is that they tend to overbuild, and aerial photography of highway networks in the United States will reveal some hilarious and tremendously expensive examples of enthusiasm running away with common sense.

A second major and widespread defect in most planning is the failure to consider the implications of a development in one field for activities in another. In economic terms, this is the failure to equitably internalize costs and benefits. For example, the current plan to build a U.S. supersonic transport fleet of 500 planes by the fall of 1978 seems to be totally uninfluenced by and consideration of U.S. or world petroleum stocks. The explanation for this apparent planning defect, which can be found in almost all areas of activity, is that human institutions are not properly organized to consider all aspects of a problem.

An excellent example of this difficulty concerns air pollution. A principal implication of air pollution is that it is involved in the causal pathways shown in Figure 1.

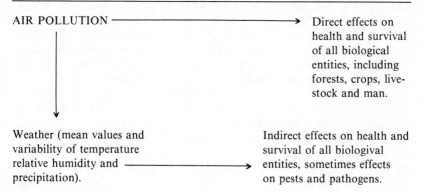

Figure 1

No single agency is set up to consider all parts of this system of cause-effect links. Meteorologists, atmospheric physicists and geophysicists are studying the effects of local, regional, and global pollution on the weather; however, it is not part of their responsibility to consider the implications of smog-altered weather on crop production, insect pests, diseases, forest production, or human health. Similarly, epidemiologists, entomologists, agronomists, and many others have been concerned about the effects of weather on biological systems for a long time, but have not extended this consideration to include the effects of atmospheric turbidity on weather systems. Thus no single agency is analyzing and predicting the effects of smog on weather, and hence of crop production, or influenza epidemics. In general, all human institutions are too discipline-oriented to deal effectively with large-scale decision-making in which the central problems of ten fall into the cracks between desciplines. Thus governments tend to be organized into departments of Agriculture, Transportation, Health, Education and Welfare, Interior, Urban Development, and universities have separate Departments of Economics, Zoology, Mathematics, and so on. Then exactly whose responsibility is it to establish the relation between the degree of smog emission from cars, and the amount of crop loss caused by a lowered number of day degrees of heat in a season resulting from smog cutting off incident solar radiation? For many such problems it is difficult to conceive of an agency which would have primary responsibility, yet this type of question is clearly crucial for the future of mankind.

This lack of integrated systems planning has particularly frightening implications in the area of land use planning. It is well-known that prime agricultural land is being converted to urban use in the United States at a fearful rate. To illustrate, only 6.7 million acres of the 100 million acres in California are prime agricultural land. Because this is converted to urban use at the rate of about 0.2 acres for each person added to the population, and since about 15 million additional people are projected for the California population by the year 2000, the loss of prime farmland will be about 0.2 x 15 million acres, or about 3.0 million acres. The prevailing theory is that this can be compensated for by increase in productivity per acre of the remaining 3.7 million acres, and by conversion of 2.0 million non-prime acres to agriculture by means of irrigation. However there are two extremely important hidden assumptions in this line of reasoning. One is that energy will be available to support ever-increasing inputs to agricultural technology. The second is that weather will remain about the same, and therefore crop production can be kept at a high level. But experts in the effects of global pollution on the weather and on world crude oil stocks see difficulties ahead within a few decades in both these areas. Thus, through failure to take a systems view of planning, plans are being made—on which all our lives depend—which fail to take into consideration all the relevant information.

Another basic defect in all planning is the failure to take the long view, to look ahead a sufficient number of years. Frequently, planners tacitly assume that humanity will not remain on this planet for more than another 150 years, and therefore it is unnecessary to worry about the depletion of materials critical to our form of civilization. Also, planning often assumes that continued existence on this planet will be made possible by forms of technology not yet known. It is worthwhile to consider both these alternatives with extreme care, and with no appeal to wishful thinking.

First, it is worthwhile documenting the statement that humanity is, in effect, planning itself out of existence in 150 years. This statement is based on the fact that a wide variety of materials absolutely critical to the maintenance of civilization as we know it will be gone by about the year 2120. This is true for wood, water, fuel (coal and oil), and many of the metals: nickel, silver, tin, chromium. Rather than spelling out the arithmetic on all of these resources the figures on chromium, an essential input to the steel industry, will serve as an example. In round numbers, estimates of the chromium oxide resources left in the world range from a low of 300 to a high of 1200 million tons. Of this, about 200 million tons will have been used by the year 2000. By that year, the total noncommunist world use rate will be about 9 million tons a year. Thus, if the low estimate is correct, all chromium oxide will be gone 11 years after the year 2000, and if the high estimate is correct, it will take 111 years. Therefore we shall be out of chromium oxide by some date between 2011 and 2111. While the dates are different, the situation is basically the same for a wide variety of resources.

Where does this leave us? Only four possibilities seem open in principle. The first is for a mass exodus from this planet to some other planet, which we can then deplete of resources. Thus the process which began with the rape of the Middle East, North Africa, North India and China would merely be extended to the universe. This is infeasible, it turns out, because of the exorbitant energy costs of sending billions of people off this planet in rockets. The second possibility is to somehow recycle existing resources so they can be used repeatedly. This creates a massive energy demand, particularly where the population density is high. Even with atomic energy it might not be possible to meet this demand because of the resultant thermal pollution. The third possibility is that we will be saved by technological revolution, which will allow us to meet all our material needs with some cheap and ubiquitous substance. Again, the immense thermal pollution that this would create may render this option infeasible. Finally, we are left with the option of conservation: that is, sharply reduced use rates agreed to by all countries. This seems to be the only option free from monumental hazards, and the only one where we can be reasonably certain the strategy is even possible.

Another defect in almost all planning is the failure to consider the possible existence of asymptotes imposing natural limits on processes. For example, the wholesale conversion of farmland to urban uses now going on in the United States seems to ignore the fact that it takes a certain minimum amount of land to raise the food required by each human being. This irreducible minimum is set by caloric constraints over which mankind has absolutely no control. That is, there is only a certain amount of solar radiation that hits any unit of the earth's surface in a day, and plants have a fixed upper limit to their efficiency in processing this energy into tissue, and livestock have a fixed upper limit to their efficiency in converting plant tissue to animal tissue.

In a surprising number of types of social activity, we have failed to record and analyze the history of past situations in sufficient detail to know exactly what happened as a consequence of a given strategy or policy. Thus much planning is based on the implicit assumption that certain types of activities are invariably good, when in fact this assumption is conventional wisdom, not a fact based on careful examination of experience. There are a truly remarkable number of instances in history where something has been done a certain way for decades or centuries in the belief that the conventional approach was unquestionably the optimal approach. However, no experiments or comparative examination of the histories resulting from other approaches had ever been conducted, so there was no way of knowing that the conventional wisdom was defective.

Three different examples will make the point. First, it is a widely held tenet of the conventional wisdom that insect pests are controlled by the use of insecticides. Yet few people use check plots to compare the results of using insecticides with what would have happened if no insecticides had been used. Only some particularly dramatic situations, as where pests vanish with the cessation of pesticide use rather than the inception of pesticide use, have led to reexamination of the conventional wisdom. Also, in forested areas where pest outbreaks by the spruce budworm formerly occurred in a 36 or 72 year cycle, the inception of regular spraying has created an historically novel situation where there is a pest outbreak almost continuously. Second, as white men emigrated from Europe to open up other continents, they were faced with two alternate strategies: exploit native plants and animals where they found them, or replace native plants and animals with livestock and grains imported from Europe. Historically there has been heavy reliance on the latter strategy, without considering the possibility that native plants and animal communities had been selected for eons to maximize the efficiency of energy flow per unit of land area. Only recent South African experience where, instead of cattle, native animals have been used for food has caused people seriously to examine the logical foundations of existing land use strategies. Third, most people naturally assume that the quickest way to get anywhere is to use the fastest method of transportation available. It is rarely recognized that the slowest method of travel is often to use the fastest type of vehicle. It is usually true that in order to use the fastest type of vehicle one has to spend so much time catching it, and getting from it to the ultimate destination, that it gives the slowest portal-to-portal mean trip velocity. For example, in a rush hour in mid-town Manhattan, it is not worthwhile to catch a cab unless one is to travel a distance of at least 2.5 miles, because of the time lost in hailing a cab. Thus unless one is going farther than 2.5 miles, it is faster to walk. Similarly, because of the great distance from city to airport, and from airport to city, train or bus will often beat aircraft portal-to-portal time unless the total distance is several hundred miles. On many long aircraft trips involving three different air segments, only five or six of seventeen hours goes into actual flight. For 175-mph inter-city trains, one would have to go about 350 miles before aircraft were the preferred mode of travel to produce minimum trip time.

The reason for bad choices, therefore, is often that no one has taken the trouble to keep a careful record of what has happened in the past in order that the record could serve as a basis for future strategy decision-making. Typically, as we have seen, no one knows exactly what happened as a consequence of using pesticides, or harvesting cattle instead of buffalo, or taking a cab instead of walking. That is, strategy decisions are commonly based on assumptions rather than any hard data. To a remarkable extent, this same feature permeates the strategy decision-making process by large organizations which often follow conventional choices rather than making an objective analysis.

Indeed, a remarkably common feature of the executive and policy-making groups in all organizations is that they maintain a climate of "acceptable" opinions. In decision-making groups within big government, big business and big universities certain types of views are simply not acceptable and are almost never discussed. For example, " our " group is right, "their" group is wrong. Frequently, if "our" subgroup lacks sufficient information about a problem area outside our range of competence, we add staff into "our" subgroup who will bring us this competence or expertise. It is rarely argued within "our" group that we should solve our deficiency in expertise by promoting cooperation and information exchange with "their" subgroup. Thus powerful social pressures operating within large institutions tend to suppress lateral information flow between parts of the institution. This produces compartmentalization of the decision-making apparatus. Also, of course, this compartmentalization and set of social pressures operates to suppress and inhibit the critical reexamination of policy, and thus leads to the perpetuation of mistaken views.

Associated with the preceding problem is the lack of data-interpretation agencies in society. Most people assume that because governmental agencies and others collect great masses of data someone makes intelligent use of these data. This is not necessarily the case. Many data-collection agencies regard the collection *per se* of the data as their sole responsibility, and assume that someone else will analyze the data and determine their significance. Other agencies, of course, assume that the data-collection agency will analyze the data it has collected. The result is that often *no* agency assumes responsibility for analyzing data already collected. Thus an acute problem developing in society, which would be revealed by a penetrating analysis of government data, often passes unsuspected because no one is adequately analyzing the data. An interesting consequence of this situation is that it is often left to private individuals to alert the public to some danger which these individuals have learned about through persual of government documents. An example of this is the failure of government agencies to analyze adequately the relationship between air pollution and respiratory diseases, a remarkably difficult task almost beyond the financial backing for data analysis by any private agency.

A difficulty in much planning is that by convention overall analyses of our society tend to be conducted by economists, who follow the flow of money rather than energy. In the last analysis it is energy flow, rather than money, which is the key measure of what is happening in the entire social system. Thus a knowledge of energy flow patterns and factors determining the efficiency of energy flow would shed a new light on the relative desirability of alternative courses of action. The reason for it not yet being glaringly apparent that energy is a more important systems measure than money is that only recently have we become aware of the fact that energy availability might become limiting for the system.

Still another difficulty with much of planning is the failure to recognize the existence of cumulative effects and time lags. What this means is that some process which might have immensely important ultimate effects may operate for a considerable period of time before it begins to reveal its effects. By the time there is widespread recognition that the process operates at all, it may be very late to take the action necessary to prevent some large-scale calamity. Thus society needs an extraordinarily sensitive ability to look ahead and discern possible catastrophes in the future. An example of this type of phenomenon is lung-disease death rates, which are rising rapidly, most likely (at least in part) in response to environmental conditions to which the lungs were exposed some time back. Therefore, even if the causes of lung diseases were dealt with now there would probably for some time continue to be a considerable increase in the number of deaths caused by lung diseases.

Another very important defect in planning results from the extreme caution bred into all scientists. While many scientists may recognize some phenomenon as a possible source of calamity, they are nervous about calling attention to this fact until the evidence indicates very strongly that the phenomenon is a possible source of widespread danger. The difficulty with this traditionally cautious attitude is that some of the phenomena in question may have such enormous implications for the future of all mankind that it is unwise to let caution blunt the usefulness of an early-warning system. There are several examples at present of phenomena which, if the suspicions of specialists are correct, are of immense importance for the future of mankind. In each case there should be far more widespread knowledge and understanding of the phenomenon, in order to create the sort of political pressure required to fund studies on an adequate scale and regulate the phenomenon. Examples are the possible effects of pesticides in cutting down photosynthesis of ocean algae, the effects of pesticides on humans, and the effects of fine particles in the atmosphere on changes in regional and global weather.

It is bad enough that there are so many defects in the planning mechanisms *per se*, but there are also problems that would impede the application of planning, even if the planning itself were absolutely omniscient and prescient.

One of the major obstacles to the application of plans is that our society offers no economic incentive to conserve anything. For example, a person is an economic martyr if he purchases farmland for farming. It is about half as economically rewarding to purchase farmland to keep it in farming as it is to purchase an average share of common stock. What is even more discouraging is that one of the better investment opportunities in our society is to purchase prime farmland for conversion to urban use. The faster the conversion, the more lucrative the return, on a per-cent-per-year basis. Thus there is an extremely powerful motive to convert immense amounts of farmland to urban use quickly. Society could thus be trapped into starvation because of two types of situations that would conceal the danger in this conversion. First, time lags in most social cause-effect systems, shortages of food and tremendous increases in food prices would not immediately show up after too much farm land had been taken out of production. Second, weather changes normally produce year-to-year variations in production which are not easily detected. As urbanization covers more and more of the world, there will be an increasing tendency for weather changes to move in the direction of more inclement weather and lower crop production. Thus, again because of lags, the full impact of pollution on the weather would not be apparent immediately, but only long after much farmland had been converted to urban use. That is, crop yields per acre would continue to drop after much of the farmland ever to be sold had been sold, so that society would have overestimated the yield per acre of the remainder of that farmland.

Still another impediment to the implementation of plans is the difficulty of assembling data to support arguments as to why developments should not occur. It is typically easy to convince an audience of the benefits to accrue from building houses on farmland, seashore, range land, wheat farms or orchards. Though these arguments can often be shown to be spurious, it takes sophisticated economic analysis and a lot of data to demonstrate that real costs may exceed supposed benefits. Of course, sophisticated analyses and appropriate data are often unavailable at the crucial moment. For example, a typical argument of developers is that if an urban area expands, this will result in a "broadening of the tax base" so that taxes per taxpayer will be lower for everyone. This argument is the opposite of the truth. But to expose the fallacy of this line of argument it takes data on the cash input and output of a large sample of metropolitan areas plus sophistication in the analysis of these data.

For example, from analyzing the data published by the office of the State Comptroller of California, we obtain the information in Table 1 on tax revenues and expenditures of various-sized municipalities in the state.

Table 1. Some Municipal Tax Revenues and Expenses for Selected California Cities in Year Ending June 30, 1967 as a Function of Urban Population

Mean City Size (June 30, 1967)	Cities in Sample	Total Local Revenues Per Capita	Public Works Expenditures Per Capita	Police Protection Per Capita
2,799,500	1	126.59	32.34	22.39
713,600	2	234.22	26.67	19.93
385,900	3	141.29	26.35	18.19
179,831	4	102.85	27.83	17.08
131,340	5	107.53	29.04	14.92
96,929	10	83.92	24.91	13.87

These figures scarcely support the conclusion that larger size leads to a lowered tax rate. The figures in this table represent an oversimplification of the situation. Tax rates probably depend not only on city size but also on density and growth rate. Therefore the high tax revenue per capita shown in the second pair of cities is because of San Francisco, which has a higher density than Los Angeles, but Los Angeles is at the core of a metropolitan area with a larger total population. Notice that with bigger and bigger cities the general trend is toward an increase in tax dollars paid out per person for municipal services.

A major impediment to implementation of planning is the strong set of economic forces that lead to maximum technologically feasible rates of exploitation of a resource, right up to the time it is totally exhausted. A particularly horrifying phenomenon can occur when a group of sharks discover a large amount of prospective food, as when an aircraft or a large ship is sinking, with many people in the water and a great deal of commotion. The commotion may attract a few sharks that make an initial attack which leads to a great deal of blood in the water, which then attracts a greater number of sharks that gradually become frenzied because of the large amount of blood and great commotion. Finally, the sharks become crazed and tear big chunks out of anything in their vicinity, including each other. This phenomenon is called a feeding frenzy. In thinking about this phenomenon one might conclude, "My God! Thank heaven I am a member of a species that would behave more rationally than that! "Really? When all resources are running out, will man, the pinnacle of biological evolution, really behave in a more rational fashion than the sharks? What is the evidence?

Writers on future trends in resource use and exploitation continue to assume that as it becomes clear that a resource is being wiped out, use rates will ease. For example, M. King Hubbert* has assumed that as it becomes clear that the United States is running the world out of petroleum, there will be a tapering-off of use rates. However, there is no historical precedent for conservation of a major resource as it became obvious that the resource was being wiped out. The response to precipitous declines in buffalo in the American West and blue whales in the oceans was to harvest both resources harder than ever, up to the point at which they were almost extinct— and it was no longer economically worthwhile to harvest them. There were perhaps 80 million buffalo in the American West in 1800. The stocks were gradually depleted until almost the entire herd was annihilated in a veritable orgy of wanton and spectacularly wasteful destruction between 1868 and 1874, during which time about seven million were killed each year. The same fate befell the Nantucket whaling industry, and in modern times, the blue and fin

*Committee on Resources and Man, NAS-NRC, *Resources and Man*. San Francisco: W. H. Freeman, 1969. pp. 157-242.

whale stocks. Far from economic forces operating to induce conservation of these common property resources, it was economic motives
which were invoked to hasten their destruction. The argument was that
the whaling nations could not justify their great investment in equipment
unless they maintained large kills, even when this was clearly driving the
stocks to the verge of extinction. If this historical pattern repeats itself,
or if we do not take legislative action to prevent it from being repeated,
then the same thing will happen to world stocks of crude oil, coal,
uranium ores and other critical resources in their turn. There is no
economic reason why this pattern of annihilation should not operate for
any resource. All economic forces operate to promote and hasten annihilation; none operate against it. For example, suppose the capital in
equipment to harvest a resource heavily costs 20-million dollars and is
completely worn out in 20 years. Then, if there is a choice between
annihilating the resource in 20 years with 20-million dollars worth of
equipment, or in 60 years with replacement of the equipment twice for a
total cost of 60-million dollars, clearly the most economic strategy is to
annihilate the resource in 20 years. This is an extremely important
point. The laws of the economic market place do not offer any reason
for saving anything, and it is hiding one's head in the sand to assume
they do. Neither economic theory nor the history of any exploited
resource in the past offers any hope that economic forces by themselves
will act to conserve anything. Typically, ruinous exploitation of
resources in the past ceased only when a resource had become so scarce
that it was no longer economically rewarding to exploit it. However, for
some resources, at that point of exploitation the resource was so scarce
that it was on the margin of extinction and never recovered.

An interesting example of the failure to see the implications of planning in one area for phenomena in another is the shortage of major
parks and wilderness areas inside of, or very close to, most large cities.
This indicates that there is also a failure to recognize that parks have
implications not only for land use but also for mental health, stress, the
behavior of an urban population and the physical climate of the city,
and hence the infectivity and lifetimes of upper-respiratory viral particles in air. It is now known that parks and trees ameliorate day-to-day
and hour-to-hour climatic changes in the area (this is why deserts are so
hot in the daytime and cold at night). For example, cities in semitropical
or tropical climates get terribly hot, particularly in the city core, unless
there are parks and trees to keep the temperature down during the
hottest part of the day. The trees keep the temperature down by converting water to water vapor at the surface of their leaves, and thus act
as giant refrigerators. (Refrigerators also function on the principle that
heat is used up, or temperature lowered, by conversion of a liquid to a
gas.) The significance of this effect of trees on climate is that human
behavior responds to temperature and humidity, the proclivity to vio-

lence being greatest in very hot, humid weather. Further, the viral particles which cause influenza have the greatest infectivity and lifetime in air when the air is dry. In the wintertime air is too dry in big cities unless something is adding moisture to the air, such as humidifiers or trees. Thus parks and trees have much more than an aesthetic significance in a city core.

The point that emerges from this discussion of planning is, simply, that those agencies responsible for making decisions about the present and the future should properly have to consider a full spectrum of costs and benefits in their analyses—including the complete array of social, environmental, health and other costs—and they are structured in such a way that th's is all but impossible. There is practically no way or provision within the present framework of planning agencies to accomplish comprehensive planning. Because of compartmentalization which may increase the *depth* in which some aspects of planning problems are studied, *breadth* has been sacrificed. And, like it or not, most environmental problems are in interface areas between disciplines, and absolutely require the free communication and removal of boundaries between departments, bureaus and other administrative units.

Planning should be comprehensive and include all pertinent information from many disciplines, yet at present we do not have an institution capable of ensuring that this will happen. What is clearly needed is a planning body which includes experts from many specialities who can provide an overview of all planning activities and their implications for both the short and the long term. Very few countries or regions are politically prepared to establish such an agency, because local control would be weakened in those instances where a subregion could be seen to engage in activities which were not in the best interests of the region as a whole.

The Only Hope for the Future

At this point it must be clear to the reader that there really *is* an environmental crisis, which is serious enough now, but which will rapidly get more serious unless appropriate action is taken. However, the situation is anything but hopeless. If we have been successful in our discussion, then perhaps we have convinced the reader that a wide variety of problems actually stem from a relatively small number of causes. Thus, for example, pollution and the rapid depletion of our energy resources are merely different symptoms of more underlying problems: population and the profligately wasteful life style into which we have unthinkingly drifted—so that we waste crude oil, land, coal, lumber and almost everything else. We have tried to show that the twin basic problems of this profligate waste and runaway population growth are, in turn, both products of an underlying cause of all our problems: a set of personal attitudes and institutional decision-making procedures that make it difficult for us to make individual or collective rational decisions about much of anything.

Most readers will be convinced by comparing the problems as we have posed them with the solutions as we propose them here, that although many of the solutions seem unconventional or unacceptable, they are mandatory and must be fought for with vigor. After all, anyone who has spent any time in the seats of government will have quickly become aware that there are many lobbyists for interests other than the future of mankind who are defending and advocating *their* causes and interests with vigor. The future of all of us should surely command the same degree of enthusiasm!

The first and most basic problem we must deal with is people's attitudes. Thinking must be changed with respect to children, property, land, agriculture, the future, and the delusion of grandeur in which all of us are now ensnared. What a child represents at present has a wide variety of meanings to different people. Sometimes a child is treasured, sometimes it is regarded as an unfortunately accidental consequence of sex, sometimes as security for the old age of a parent who has few friends, and sometimes as a source of economic support from the government to a poor family on welfare. We hold it to be self-evident that only one attitude of a parent to a child implies an optimal life for the child: the child must have been born because it was wanted, in advance. In the most extreme opposite situation, where the child was positively not wanted in advance and was rejected by one or both parents after birth, the consequences for all of society can be frightening. Many of the most callous murderers of recent history fall into this category.

Thus it seems to be in the interest of humanity, including the child itself, that each child born should be wanted. There are three means of achieving this end. Society can provide powerful motives, through the tax system, to avoid having children unless they are really wanted; it can make it much easier to prevent conception, by funding birth-control information centers and clinics; and it can make it vastly easier to terminate an unwanted pregnancy through legislation completely legalizing abortion.

In fact, much progress is being made on all these fronts. Senator Packwood of Oregon has introduced a bill into the United States Senate which will provide a federal income tax deduction of $1000 for the first child, $750 for the second child, and no deductions for additional children after the second. This is a good bill which represents a step in the right direction by providing a powerful motive for not having three or more children. Readers should communicate their support for this measure both to Senator Packwood and to their own senators.

A variety of organizations are lobbying for legislation to study the population problem and deal with it. Readers can join this important movement by contacting Zero Population Growth, 367 State Street, Los Altos, California, 94022.

It is also important that society make freely available information on birth control and on the devices required to prevent birth. Organizations such as Planned Parenthood are performing a critically important public service and should be supported. Some critics of this position maintain it is racist and elitist, and smacks of genocide. But brown, black and yellow garbage look exactly like white and red garbage. It is important that we be absolutely clear as to what we do advocate. We believe that all couples should limit their number of offspring to two, without regard to the race, color, religion, wealth, or other attributes of the couple. This strikes us as a totally egalitarian, democratic concept, and we fail to see how it implies lack of fair treatment of any particular group in society because it specifically advocates equal treatment for all. We fail to see how we can be called the enemy of any particular segment of our population by arguing for a two-child limit per couple, as restriction of births increases the chance that the children of all peoples will have the best possible chance in life. What we are opposed to is poverty, and the physical and psychic starvation that springs from poverty. It seems clear to us that excessive numbers of children are at least one of the important causes contributing to poverty. A young mother with eight children has built a tremendously strong cage for herself and her children, we believe, from which it is extremely difficult to escape.

We are tremendously impressed by the value of legalized abortions, in all states of the United States, and in all countries. All of us have met parents who are quick to explain that one or more of their children was the product of one, or several, birth-control methods that somehow failed. It is a statistical fact that all birth-control methods can fail, although the probability varies for the different methods. Thus abortion at an early stage in pregnancy becomes the last line of defense against the unwanted child. Hawaii, New York, and other states now have legalized abortion legislation, and early indications make it clear how tremendous the demand was for this social service.

The most important component of planning for tomorrow is to reduce the pressures on the environment by the most direct means possible: a population policy which will bring an end to population growth. It is extremely important to point out that family planning is *not* a population policy: if the average family *plans* to have 3.4 children, then the world will become overrun with people, and utterly uninhabitable because of utter degradation of existence. Family planning could soon lead to the type of crowding now observed in Calcutta.

We must change our attitudes toward property, as well as children. All of us must learn to put more value on public common property relative to private property. Our present instinct on how best we can deal with the property aspect of the population-environment problem is to get our own little piece of private property, rather than to limit population. This approach is self-defeating, as the people from India could quickly demonstrate. Our position can be explained most clearly by considering a specific example. Suppose that 400 people are using a 400-acre tract of ocean beachfront, which is public, common property and unfenced. At this density, it is easy for each person to derive a great deal of enjoyment from the beach. Several different things can happen to this beach, however. One is for the beach to be purchased by a developer, who waits for the population to grow to 6400 people, then subdivides the beachfront into 1600 quarter-acre lots, each of which is purchased by a family with an average size of four people. A second possibility is for the people who enjoy the beach to grow to a population of 6400, who then share the beach which was formerly shared by 400. A third possibility is for the population not to grow, but to remain at 400. Which is the best way to deal with the population-environment problem, to buy a quarter-acre beachfront lot to escape from the other 6396 people, or for all to decide collectively that the beach was more fun when it was public, unfenced, and there were 400 people? Our position is that the latter is preferable. What is *yours*? If you agree with us, then you should be supporting legislative efforts to limit population growth!

This leads us, inexorably, to another problem: involvement with government. We have discovered—to our dismay—in lecturing all over the United States and Canada that many people, particularly young people, regard the government as *The Establishment*, which means *The Enemy*, utterly unresponsive to the public will, particularly the will of young people. One cause of this viewpoint is that a high proportion of our young people simply haven't had any contact with legislators. We shall not argue that all legislators are totally worthy of support, or are completely responsive to the public will, because this is demonstrably not so. However we know from our own experience that many legislators are dedicated, immensely energetic, idealistic people. They are well aware of the problems discussed in this book, and are motivated to do the right thing to correct the problems. However, these legislators, courageous though some of them may be, simply cannot push forward-looking legislation on population and environmental problems through their legislatures without strong evidence of public support. Unfortunately, that evidence is often lacking. It is extremely important that people concerned about the problems in this book identify those legislators (there are many of them) who share this concern, and help these men create appropriate new laws. If new legislation of intelligent, comprehensive and sound design, adequately matched to the problems is to be created, it will often take a group of dedicated amateurs who help legislators in making background research, checking prior laws and drafting bills. Thus the appropriate strategy for the reader is to watch his communications media carefully in order to identify those legislators who share his concerns. Then write, and offer your services in development of new legislation. It helps if in the first letter you enclose copies of material discovered through your library research, indicating the way in which you can contribute to the designing of good legislation.* People concerned with the problems discussed in this book simply must get more concerned with the entire process of selecting candidates, campaigning, fund-raising and lobbying. The public cannot legitimately complain that its voice is not being heard by its elected representatives if in fact it never raises its voice.

We have mentioned that a dangerous characteristic of our civilization is the preoccupation with *Now*. This fact has all kinds of implications, all of them harmful to us and to our environment. One thing it means is that we focus on the fast buck, try to make a lot of money quickly by investing in corporations with a very high growth rate at a time when their rate of growth is fastest, then pull out and reinvest our gains in another similar situation. An implication is that we do not think enough about the possibility that the corporation in which we invest may be using its capital in such a fashion that the resources on which it depends for its growth may be destroyed by the way in which the corporation is using its money. To return to the beach example, consider the corporation that invests its money covering the beach of some tropical island with luxury resort hotels. It certainly seems possible that by "overdeveloping" the beach it may become less attractive to tourists, and profits will gradually decline. The essence of the situation is that by pursuing strategies that make sense over the short run, but do not make sense over the long run, the profitability of the corporation is high initially but then declines. Thus investors buy stock in a corporation when it is riding high, but desert the sinking ship when evidence of long-term deleterious strategies gradually appears. Indeed, the federal government contributes to this personal strategy of taking the short view on investments through the way in which income is split into income or capital gains on income tax statements. Specifically, if an investor has held a stock for six months plus one day, the profits from sale of the stock due to increase in the price of the stock can be declared for tax purposes as capital gains rather than income. Capital gains have a lower tax rate than income. The government is hardly contributing towards encouragement of the habit of taking a long view into the future when making personal choices among available strategies by having the critical time period

---

*To the reader: After you have finished this book, for example, why not mail it to your senator or Congressman? —Ed.

only six months! This time period would appear to intensify the preoccupation of the population with *Now*, rather than with a long view of the future. One simple way to deal with this problem would be to lengthen the period from six months to five or ten years. By doing this the prospective investor would be encouraged to make a careful examination of the long-term prospects of alternative investments, in order to ensure that none of the corporations were pursuing policies which would destroy the resource base on which their profitability depended.

There are a number of other ways in which the government through the use of taxes and legislation can encourage people to be more rational in their personal decisionmaking about the environment. One strategy which could have a profound effect on land use patterns would be to change the present practice of assessing all land at its highest use. In general, the current practice means that a farmer growing crops on prime agricultural land at the periphery of an urban area is taxed as if his land were being subdivided for tract housing. Thus the farmer who continues to farm at the edge of an urban area is an economic martyr if he continues to farm rather than sell his land for tract housing. There should be a reversal of this state of affairs, so that farmers at the periphery of an urban area are given a strong economic incentive for growing crops rather than an incentive to sell out to subdividers. In fact in California the Williamson Act was designed and put into operation for precisely this purpose. In general, it has become mandatory that we convert to a system of taxation and zoning strategies that operate against land speculation and urban sprawl, rather than promote them.

Another way of achieving this end is through the land bank concept. That is, the amount of land needed to make each state agriculturally self-sufficient for perpetuity is computed, and this land is zoned for agriculture permanently. The particular parcels that should be included in the agricultural land bank would be selected by beginning with the best agricultural land first, then gradually including more and more agricultural land until the bank was sufficient, adding in parcels from best to worst for agriculture.

It is possible in principle to compute the required size of such a land bank by using the following argument, in which for illustrative purposes only we use California as the sample system.

Assume that California now has 20.5 million people and 6.7 million acres of prime agricultural land are left, of which 0.2 acres are taken out of production for each person added to the population. Assume that we need 0.25 acres per person to provide an adequate diet for a California citizen. Assume further that at the time at which California runs out of food, the same thing will be happening elsewhere. Assume still further that non-prime agricultural land can be ignored in this calculation for several reasons, including gradual salinization of the soil and inability to meet price competition with urban users for imported water.

Given this particular set of numbers and this particular set of assumptions, we can calculate the size of the agricultural land bank needed to ensure agricultural self-sufficiency for California for perpetuity as shown below.

Let X represent the additional population of California in millions at the time when the prime agricultural land in millions of acres required to support the California population is just equal to the prime acreage still remaining for agricultural use. Given our numbers and our assumptions, the acreage needed to support that population of California can be obtained from this equation:

$$0.25(20.5 + X) = 6.7 - 0.2X$$

X = 3.5, and the land bank that California will need is 6.7 0.2(3.5) = 6.0 million acres.

Now, any of the assumptions or numbers in the preceding exposition could be challenged by certain experts. For example, take the assumption that 0.2 of an acre of prime land is taken out of production for each person added to the population. Analyses by different people and different professional groups give estimates of that number ranging from 0.17 acres to 2.0 acres.

However, if groups of experts were locked in a room for awhile, surely they could come to an agreement on the issues and specific values needed to serve as the basis for legislation. However, should the experts decide they cannot arrive at a consensus, this would reveal that more data were needed.

Of course in a thorough and sophisticated application of the land bank concept, we would use a calculation that takes into consideration all categories of land and all land uses, including urban and transportation use, grazing, field and truck crops, forestry, wilderness recreation, parks, *et cetera*.

Another economic means by which government can prevent wasteful dissipation of natural resources is to force price increases on scarce items, or impose taxes according to a scale which rises as an item becomes scarcer. For example, it is interesting to contemplate what would happen if the government were suddenly to pass a law causing a doubling in the price of gasoline, newsprint, lumber, nickel or chromium. Over the long term no one would suffer, as these materials would simply be used with double the existing efficiency. The information content of newspapers would double or newsprint would be recycled, the efficiency of automobile engines would double, pollution caused by pulp mills and cars would drop, and so on. It is difficult to see what deleterious long-term costs would be associated with such price manipulation.

However, it is easy to see that such suggestions would be opposed by those people with a traditional, short-term, economic view of resource use.

Still another means by which government can foster more enlightened thinking about the future is to provide corporations with economic incentives to switch from one type of manufacturing to another. This is of course entirely feasible, as during a war when automobile manufacturers switch to tank production. An important case in point at the moment is the aerospace industry. Instead of encouraging this industry to develop the supersonic transport—which represents disaster for everyone, including the aerospace industry—the government should be subsidizing the conversion of the industry to mass production of high-speed intercity and intracity trains of completely novel types.

An important means by which the government could help solve our present irrational transportation system problems would be to use gasoline taxes to subsidize the development of high-speed rail systems. This plan is being considered by some states and regions of the country, but because of a powerful array of lobbyists favoring highway construction, the amount of money channeled into these systems will probably be relatively small. If rail systems could move between cities at speeds in excess of 175 miles per hour, then because they moved from urban core to urban core instead of from airport to airport, they would exceed mean doorstep-to-doorstep trip speeds at distances of up to 350 miles.

It has become desperately necessary that the government develop new types of planning and regulatory agencies. Indeed, corporations are also in need of such agencies. These agencies would be designed for the express purpose of promoting lateral information flow from discipline to discipline, so that we could avoid the present difficulties in which planning is made by one discipline on the basis of hidden implicit assumptions that would be challenged by other disciplines.

Society needs to become more sophisticated with respect to the internalization of costs and benefits. However, new types of agencies and institutions designed for long-range planning with respect to environmental effects would provide much of the needed information about how to internalize costs and benefits as a side benefit of their research. It is clear that society now has a compelling need for such new kinds of institutions that make plans for the future, assess the costs and benefits of other agencies' plans, and serve as catastrophe-warning agencies. Existing regulatory institutions need to be modified so that there is more careful followup, monitoring and documentation of the consequences of taking various socially important actions. By these means, it might be possible to avoid the variety of types of disaster toward which humanity is now lurching.

There needs to be considerable innovation in the area of making decisions in the face of uncertainty. If there were a formalized and institutionalized approach to making decisions in the face of incomplete information, or some uncertainty about the significance of existing information, we would be less likely to overlook impending disasters.

One approach to making decisions on an inadequate basis is to reason as follows. Suppose we make a prediction, and action is or is not taken on the basis of the prediction, four possible situations can occur: (1) the prediction is correct, and the appropriate action is taken on the basis of the correct decision; (2) the prediction is correct, but the appropriate action is not taken; (3) the prediction is incorrect, but the action is taken that would have been appropriate if the decision were correct; and (4) the prediction is incorrect, and no action is taken.

Now for each of these four situations, it is possible to make quite complete cost-benefit analyses in advance of any action being taken. Having made these compilations of all possible costs and all possible benefits for each of the four possible alternatives, we can ask if all the costs and benefits associated with possibilities (1) and (3) make their total benefits greater than the total benefits relative to costs associated with (2) and (4). Thus it may turn out that even if we are not sure that a prediction is correct, its implications are so important if it is correct that it is worthwhile acting as if it were correct. That is, the costs associated with acting as if the prediction is correct, when in fact it is not correct, are so small that they are outweighed by the costs of not acting, should the prediction be correct.

Because we live in a society that is basically governed by money, the solution for our failure to conserve necessary resources is to provide economic incentives for conservation. Economic motives (preferably incentives) should also be employed to improve the efficiency with which energy is used. Government should also provide strong economic incentives for alternative ways of communicating, transporting or manufacturing that use materials at a much lower rate. For example, not all the advertisements in a newspaper are of interest to all readers. The government might encourage newspapers to send to each household only those advertisements that were requested for video screen display in the home, by dialing of a predetermined telephone number. Thus the newspaper might store advertisements in a central data bank for a length of time that varied with the rate paid by each advertiser. A telephone request might begin first with the number of the advertising office, then an additional number for the category of advertisement which was to be scanned on the video screen in the home. Such a system would result in an immense savings in the amount of paper required by newspapers but would have no effect on the usefulness of the advertisement system, or on the number of people employed in the advertising office. No material would be wasted because most homes already have telephones and television sets.

In short, while the future of environmental and population problems looks somewhat bleak at present, there is much cause for optimism provided we begin immediately with an extremely aggressive and vigorous program to deal with the problems. Although there are a great many tools that we *can* use, we must also become aggressively involved in the governmental and legislative process in order to expedite the application of these tools. Time is running out.

Technological Optimists Versus Doomsayers

A large, obviously clever and extremely well-informed group of scientists is expressing great alarm about the future of mankind on this planet. They say that because resources are limited and we are polluting the planet, population growth must be stopped and, preferably, population must decrease from the present approximately four-billion people to one billion, or perhaps even less. On the other hand a large, equally clever and well-informed group of scientists is saying that the population can continue to grow for a considerable period, and all mankind's problems can be solved with novel technology.

The time has come when the issue must be faced head-on. How can two such similar groups of experts hold such widely divergent views? Both groups contain experts in every type of field, people of intelligence who in their writings and speeches indicate that both groups are familiar with the same sets of facts. No essential difference can be discovered between these two groups with respect to whether they came from an urban or rural background, the discipline in which they received training, or any other such factor. We can only conclude that the two groups differ on some issue which is basically philosophical, or even religious in character; it is important to discover what this issue is, given the magnitude of the stakes involved.

Review of the evidence leads us to conclude that the following is an essential difference. The "technological optimists" are utterly convinced that man, as a species, can solve any problem with which the species is faced. The "neo-Malthusians," in contrast, are equally convinced that there is a fixed upper limit to the availability of resources on this planet, and that this imposes limits on the magnitude of the problems this species can solve.

In fact the issue cannot be resolved with certainty, but there are a number of critical lines of evidence bearing on this difference in opinion which lead to an extremely important conclusion, or group of conclusions. First, the ability of this species to solve problems depends, in the last analysis, on the amount of energy available to us. The total amount required is rapidly becoming extremely large as the number of people increases and the amount of energy used per person increases. Another reason is that as humanity uses up more and more of the readily available sources of matter and energy on the planet, we become more dependent on sources which can only be obtained by an expenditure of even more energy. Our increasing dependence on ores which contain low proportions of useful material, and which are covered by deep rock overburden, is an example. By the time we have totally exhausted our supplies of crude oil and coal, the amount of energy required by humanity will be equivalent to very roughly 200-billion barrels of crude oil a year, if present trends continue. Several lines of argument and different types of evidence indicate that present trends will continue. The only type of energy source which can in principle yield this much energy, given current scientific knowledge and materials requirements, is nuclear energy. Thus the technological optimists are assuming that it is a *certainty* that nuclear sources can be made to yield this much energy in a controlled, industrially and agriculturally useful fashion. But this *is* not a certainty. If one asks many experts about the probability that nuclear energy will be able to meet demand on the necessary scale, he will obtain a wide variety of estimates. But we have not yet met anyone who will assert that the probability of getting both the breeder reactor and the controlled fusion reaction operating on this scale is 100 percent.

The deeper issue here is whether we can plan *with certainty* for the solution of *any* extremely complex problem, given *limited time* in which to solve it. There is both historical and analytical evidence bearing on this point. A well-known historical example, in which a very large team of experts was assembled to produce a technological miracle against a tight deadline, was the United States' program to build an atomic bomb. This program was essentially begun with a letter from Einstein to President Roosevelt in the summer of 1939, and it was not known that the project had been successful until the first atomic explosion at Alamogordo, New Mexico, on July 16, 1945. Thus the project took about six years. The important point is that on that July 16th the scientists who had built the bomb did not know with certainty what would happen *before* the explosion. Because the atomic bomb did actually work, the uncertainty that had existed among the scientists was over-shadowed by success. The point is that when a technological solution to a problem is required—by the very magnitude of the problem—to include a high level of complexity, it is difficult to predict if the solution *will* work. Indeed, recent work by Professor Forrester of the Massachusetts Institute of Technology has demonstrated that a city is such a complex system that in trying to deal with its problems, using an intuitively reasonable set of solutions, the problems may actually become worse.

We must conclude, in the last analysis, that the technological optimists are gambling. Even though constantly rising world human populations coupled with constantly rising energy consumption per capita are increasing the magnitude of the problems that mankind must solve some day, they are gambling that it is *certain* that we can solve those problems. This does not seem prudent to us. It would appear that the optimal strategy is to prevent a problem from arising until *after* we know for certain that a solution is available. We should not let a problem intensify on the gamble that a solution can be found when it is absolutely needed. Indeed, despite the misgivings of many experts, some people are so certain that atomic energy will supply vast amounts of energy when it is needed, three or four decades from now, that they are not nervous about the rather striking under-funding of the research programs required to develop breeder and fusion reactors.

In practical terms, what this means is that negative population growth (declining population) is the only rational international strategy until after we are sure that controllable nuclear fusion and fast breeder reactors are functional realities. Furthermore, these energy sources must be able to provide massive amounts of energy without unacceptable side-effects such as release of tritium or other radioactive materials, or excessive heating of the world's waters through the dissipation of waste heat.

To let the world population mushroom to 10 or 15 billion people before we have controlled nuclear fusion is gambling with intolerably large stakes. We can always make a population of 3.5 billion people increase with minimal trauma if we should decide we want to do that. On the other hand, a drop in population from 10 of 15 billion to 1 to 4 billion in a short time would be accompanied by unimaginable trauma.

Another problem which the technological optimists have ignored is that, in addition to the tremendous problems we might have if nuclear energy does not materialize on the scale hoped for, there are a number of inevitable problems associated with high rates of population increase. The essential difficulty is that high rates of population increase, coupled with a high standard of social services such as education, medical and health services, and governmental and legal services, put an immense burden on the taxpayer. And the impact on human senses of cities that are three or four times as large or as crowded as they are today would probably be less than desirable.

The Future

What will life be like in the future? At present, mankind does not seem to have a very clear future. What we see are probably four alternate futures, and it is important to understand the costs and benefits associated with the various options open to us.

The first alternative is that the world population size drops quickly from about four billion, the present approximate number, to between one and two billion people; and subsequently, we discover that the controlled nuclear fusion process is feasible, so the population begins to rise again. The principle cost in this option is the trauma involved in a tremendous population decrease, which might not have been necessary. The magnitude of the trauma will be great because a high proportion of the entire population now consists of young women of child-bearing ages, or shortly to be of child-bearing ages—a situation that has resulted from the extremely high rate of population growth the world has recently experienced. If the total number of children of American women stabilizes at an average of 3.4 children, the U.S. population in 2000 A.D. will be 356 million. If it stabilizes at 2.45 children per woman, the population in the year 2000 will be 280 million. This gives us some idea of the magnitude of our problem. To make the U.S. population actually decline in the next three decades, each woman from now on would have to limit her children, on the average, to about one. So this is the dilemma that we, in America, have worked ourselves into by allowing our population to grow too rapidly in recent years! But this problem is trivial compared to that in the developing countries. By 1966 the birth rate for U.S. women had dropped to about 19.4 per thousand people. In Taiwan, for example, the corresponding statistic for 1965 was about 32!

The second option is that the world population drops, and then it becomes evident that the controlled nuclear fusion and breeder reactors cannot supply very large amounts of energy to mankind on a continuing basis, because of technological difficulties in making the processes acceptably safe in terms of isotope or thermal or other pollution. In this case, it will have turned out that the voluntary drop in population was utterly necessary.

The third option is that we do not decide to reduce the population, are lucky, and can develop massive new sources of energy, presumably nuclear.

The fourth possibility is that the population grows to between 10 and 20 billion people in the world and is not lucky. Energy runs out, the carrying capacity of the planet drops, and there is a sudden traumatic drop in world population. However the remaining people, saddened and made wiser by the unimaginable disaster, learn to live in an equilibrium state with energy they can acquire on a continuing basis. The future in this case would be that of a high technology variant of a world as it was in 1800 or 1850. Draft horses, for example, would probably figure much more prominently in that world than they do at present.

What we now want to consider is the third and fourth options, in which a considerably larger human population than at present is made possible by the development of a massive nuclear power capability. What kind of a world would that be? Would it be pleasant? The answers to such questions are important, because it may turn out that even if we could support twenty billion people on the world, we would not want to because that type of life would not be worth living.

Several rather simple arguments can be invoked to give an idea of what such a world would be like. All of us can make a number of observations about various trends in the world during the last few decades, and extrapolating those trends can yield insights into the future.

As the world population density rises, the size of all organizations increases, and the volume of messages moving around in organizations rises rapidly, in order to solve problems and maintain integration. The rate of signal or message flow becomes so great that one of two things happens. Either many of the messages intended for a recipient are simply not received by him because he doesn't have enough time to read or hear them all; or, he does read and hear them all by working harder, faster, and longer hours. Either alternative leads to problems. In the former case, because many of the messages are never read, or at least are not read by the person to whom they were sent but rather by his assistants, things start going wrong. In fact, there is considerable evidence that this type of thing is now happening in all large organizations. In the latter case, life in organizations becomes very unpleasant. A simple check on this trend is to ask yourself the following questions: How much mail did I get this week, in a typical week a year ago, and in a typical week ten years ago? How much mail do I get compared to the amount my parents got when they were my age?

In short, there is reason to believe that the rate at which all our nervous systems are being bombarded with information is, or shortly will be, higher than a rate which is comfortable.

Another indication of what extreme crowding can do to people can be observed in the present conditions in Calcutta, although we must interpret the evidence with care because in Calcutta crowding is combined with extreme poverty. Calcutta is rapidly becoming uninhabitable by most Western standards. The police are paralyzed by political interference, businesses are moving out of Calcutta because of the anarchy, several different communist organizations are fighting with each other, the incidence of crime and violence is rising sharply, and the city is in the grip of poverty, disease and despair. The key point is that the population density of Calcutta has become so large, relative to the availability of resources, that the city is on the verge of total collapse all the time. All systems are being stressed to the point where they just barely function. To make the point that this is not simply the product of poverty, the same observation in principle is often made by visitors to Manhattan. The population density of an area can rise to such a level that, no matter how much wealth is in the area, the entire social system is precariously susceptible to a wide variety of continually recurring malfunctions. Strikes, electrical power failures, excessive snow, water shortages, low availability of certain kinds of equipment, supplies or technical personnel can have a devastating effect on Manhattan. Clearly, an ingenious trapper or prospector working by himself in the wilderness might better be able to ride out many types of catastrophes than if he were in Manhattan, for all its resources. Who wants to live in a social system where the density is so great that ultra-complex organizational systems are required to solve problems, such that the very complexity of these systems maximizes their vulnerability to a wide variety of failures?

Who wants to live in a social system where the density is so great that ultra-complex organizational systems are required to solve problems, such that the very complexity of these systems maximizes their vulnerability to a wide variety of failures?

However there is another, much deeper problem involved in living the sardine-can existence that would result if this planet had 10 to 20 billion people. A subtle but extremely important consequence of increased human population density is that diversity between different parts of the world is diminished, and uniformity spreads over everything. The world becomes duller, less exciting, less variable and colorful to the senses. This happens in many ways. The rarer plants and animals will become extinct, and this means less variety to look at and less variety in our diet. Our diet will also become poorer, because we shall have to eat more plant food and less animal food. This is because it takes fewer acres to grow the plant food required to feed a person than it takes to grow animal food, and when the population is 20 billion we shall be very short of acres. Also, as the population grows to 20 billion, it will be progressively more difficult to take a holiday where one can get away from it all. Everywhere one goes there will be teeming multitudes of people. The only holidays available will be the Coney Island or Black Sea type, where the beach is a seething mass of people as far as the eye can see. Different types of places, like tropical rain forests or coral reefs, will be gone. The rain forests will have been cut down for other purposes, and the coral coral reefs will have been carried home by collectors. There will be nothing rare in the world; everything rare will have been taken home by someone as a prize. Only very common things will be left, and the common things will have become very dull. This process has already become very obvious around wilderness resort areas. In order to sell as many lots as possible in a given tract of land, the first act of many developers in a forested area is to cut down the trees and bulldoze off the topsoil so that although more lots are made available, the area has the appeal of the middle of the Sahara Desert.

Who wants all this? The conclusion seems obvious. It well may be that even if we could find the energy to support 20 billion people on this planet indefinitely, we gradually would come to realize that the life style involved was so unattractive and soul-destroying that we would voluntarily decide to limit births and reduce the population to something in the one to two billion range. Why not decide that before we cover the entire landscape with houses, apartments, hotels and freeways?

Kenneth E. F. Watt received a B.A. in Biology from the University of Toronto in 1951, and a Ph.D. in Zoology in 1954 from the University of Chicago, where he specialized in ecology under Professor Thomas Park. He worked in various Canadian government organizations as a statistician and biometrician for the next decade, then moved to the University of California at Davis, where he is a Professor of Zoology and Research Systems Analyst in the Institute of Ecology. He is the author of numerous publications, including the book *Ecology and Resource Management*. He holds an honorary Doctor of Laws degree from Simon Fraser University, the Gold Medal of the Entomological Society of Canada, and the Fisheries Ecology and Management Award of the Wildlife Society, an international award which is given once each year. He is perhaps best known as the principal investigator on a very large project funded by the Ford Foundation and the U.S. National Science Foundation to begin building a mathematical model of human society, for use in computer simulation of the future consequences of various broad strategies that might be adopted by mankind.

CHAPTER 7

The Elimination of Smog

Edgardo Contini

. . . make the system correct itself!

This is a modest proposal aimed at the elimination of smog—(*and* protection of Santa Barbara's beaches against pollution, *and* release of dangerous tensions in the Middle East)—all in one, single, swift swoop.

Sometime toward the middle of July, 1969, the Senate of the State of California gave approval to a remarkable bill introduced by State Senator Nicholas C. Petris, and motivated by a most laudable objective: reduction and, eventually, elimination of smog. The task was to be approached simply and forthrightly: as of January 1, 1975 no vehicle powered by internal combustion engines could be sold in the State of California. Eyebrows were raised at the daring of the proposition; for a brief interlude, it looked as though—in the Golden State at least—the problem of smog would be handled with adequate muscle.

The exhilaration was shortlived: even before the bill could be introduced to the Assembly, the opposing vested interests—that reportedly had been caught napping—went to work. The original version of the bill was withdrawn and substituted with a far less effective one aimed at tightening of the restrictions on exhaust emission currently in force. Senator Petris, with remarkable dedication and persistence, has introduced in the Senate new legislation consistent with the original proposal during the 1970 session; its chance of adoption—with its teeth intact—is very slim.

On August 8, 1969, it was reported in the press and radio that two Los Angeles residents had instituted suits against automobile manufacturers, oil companies, the U.S. Attorney General, the Secretary of HEW, and the governors of thirty-seven states, seeking damages in the amount of $15 billion for their failure to provide with adequate smog-abating devices the automobiles that are fabricated, marketed and licensed to operate. To the best of my knowledge the audacious endeavor has been successfully squelched.

Conversely, a recent Government proposal to tax leaded gasoline—a modest effort to reduce if not smog as such at least its toxic content—has been indignantly opposed by both the automobile manufacturers *and* the labor unions.

I suspect that if a truly significant effort to eliminate the internal combustion engine by restriction were seriously considered—something on the order of the Petris Bill, something that unavoidably would result in inconvenience and cost to the average user—industry and labor would be joined in their protest by the entire "silent majority"!

This should not be surprising: pressing and severe as the problem of pollution from automobile exhaust has become, it will not be successfully resolved by essentially repressive measures (as both the Petris bill and the lawsuit essentially would have been for the simple, if perhaps sad, axiom that repressive measures in a free enterprise democratic society cannot be invoked when they affect (or even just inconvenience) a majority of the population; rational and beneficial as their objectives may be, repressive measures of this kind simply are not voted in.

Since any conceivable solution to the problem of smog will affect most of us as purchasers and operators of motor vehicles, we ought to evolve more ingenious devices—incentive oriented rather than repression directed—to attack the problem. I submit that such an approach can be devised, that it could be politically palatable, and that it would prove equally effective—if not more effective—than any measure of repressive nature that might stand a reasonable chance of adoption.

Premises

Let it be postulated, for the sake of simplicity, that: (1) we are not about to give up the privileges and benefits (real and imaginary) of individual mobility that the ownership and operation of the automobile has made possible—even if air pollution in urban areas should increase above present levels; and (2) as long as we are going to retain the combustion engine as the prevalent power source for our vehicles, we are never going to fully solve the problem of air pollution in urban areas.

I know that the postulations will be challenged (especially the second by those who are engaged in developing Rube Goldberg emission control breakthroughs that, when "legalized" and "mandated," will make their inventors rich, will hold back foreign competition, will increase the cost of the car, and perhaps will even reduce exhaust emission to some degree), yet, on the strength of current evidence, the postulations must be allowed to stand if we really want to face the problem and not quibble about trivia.

As to the first postulate, car ownership in terms of percentage of population is still increasing (though it will eventually level off near the ratio of one-car-per-potential-driver) and large urban concentrations—those that are more susceptible to smog—are continuously growing in extent and, more recently, in density; this trend is likely to continue into the foreseeable future: contiguous "conurbations" of 20-, 30-, 50-million residents are unflinchingly anticipated. While the introduction of more effective means of mass transportation is desirable and probable, its effect as a smog abater is not likely to be very significant. At least for the immediate future, mass transit cannot be expected to become popular or effective in the suburban areas that were developed—and shaped—by the private automobile, and that represent, by now, a major portion of our urban structure.

The second postulate is supported by the evidence that smog levels are not decreasing despite all the restrictions and requirements that have been imposed in recent years on combustion-engine exhaust emission. The percentage of pollution reduction achieved is obviously offset by the percentage of traffic increase. At most, it can be conceded that things are possibly not as bad as they might otherwise have been (though even of this we cannot be quite sure: some authorities suggest that, so far, we may have been concerned with control of the wrong component of exhaust gases and that the real culprit is still at large). In any event, there is no reasonable justification for confidence that the problem of air pollution will ever be solved by exhaust control measures.

Now, let's formulate two more postulates—better, perhaps, "self-evident truths"—so as to have all bases covered: (1) if we are halfway sane, we should desperately want to get rid of smog, because it is unhealthyy and ugly-looking, and, because by reducing the level of brilliancy of our environment, it makes all of us duller; and, (2) the elimination of smog has had a low rating in the listing of national priorities. We seem to presume that sending a few hardy individuals to the moon will get us more points in world opinion than making life healthier and more comfortable for our urban population. We cannot count on federal appropriations for a crash program that will "get rid of smog by 19?? at the latest, and certainly before the Russians do it!"

One final postulate: if we really want to—and if we commit adequate resources to the task—we *can* develop a satisfactory alternative to the internal combustion engine. I am in no position to submit technical support to this proposition, yet the success of our space program—an infinitely more complex task—should be adequate evidence that, given the desire and the commitment, we can indeed achieve any technological objective that we set for ourselves.

So, in summary
1.   We are going to keep on driving.
2.   Smog is going to increase.
3.   We should want to get rid of smog.
4.   A crash program as a matter of national policy is unlikely.

We must find an alternative way out. Such a way out is the thrust of this proposal.

A Way Out

The solution would really be very simple if we could devise a way to: (1) energize the "system" (that is, the sum total of the interests, investments, resources, regulations, restraints et cetera, that constitute mobility by private automobile), so that it will *within itself* motivate smog abatement developments; and (2) accomplish this objective by an approach that is innovative and imaginative, and yet consistent with national precedent and with political feasibility. The proposal, based upon these premises is, in essence, as follows:

First, air—clean air—will be declared by the government (preferably by the federal government, otherwise the government of one of the large states) a public asset, and anyone who utilizes clean air and returns it as "dirty" air to the common reservoir will be charged a "use fee," somewhat as anyone visiting a national park must pay a nominal entrance charge.

Second, the fees collected from "air use" are specifically and exclusively allocated to "incentive funds" that will be distributed to those who are willing to utilize for private transportation those products of new technology that can accomplish the given objective—individual mobility—without or at a drastically reduced rate of air pollution.

These two measures, if sensitively correlated and implemented, would constitute a "stick and carrot" combination of compelling logic and impressive effectiveness.

From Carrot to Stick

Let's look at the "dimensions" of the incentives for innovation that this "stick and carrot" approach would generate if applied to means of private mobility.

Let's assume that the average "air combustion" automobile engine will be required to pay an "air use fee" starting, let's say, at $20 per year and increasing by $20 increments each year, until it levels off, ten years hence at $200 per year. Such a sliding scale would have the objective of minimizing the penalty initially but of clearly and steadily increasing the motivation for adoption of alternatives. Let's further assume that all the "air use fees" collected are distributed as a bonus to the users of vehicles that do not use or pollute air in the process of energy generation. If, by the end of the first year, only a very small number of nonpollutant vehicles (say, 1%) has been developed and put in circulation, the "rebate bonus" to each owner of such vehicles would be significant: ($20 x 100) = $2,000 for that year.

It is hard to believe that private industry would not jump into the "market vacuum" created by an incentive of such magnitude, or that it would fail to develop and produce new types of vehicles that would qualify their owners for the bonus. Conversely, the public can be expected to accept the inconveniences that may accompany the initial phases of the technological changeover if the yearly rebate bonus is of such dimension that, for the early pioneers at least, it could be counted on to entirely cover the financing cost of the new vehicles.

If the assumption of 1% at the end of the first year is too optimistic, the magnitude of the incentive would increase, thus amplifying the inducement for innovation; if it should prove conservative, so much the better. The "bonus" to each owner of a nonpolluting vehicle would be smaller, but progress toward the ultimate objective—elimination of smog—would, in effect, be ahead of schedule.

Let it be assumed that by the end of the fifth year, 50% of all cars will be of the new nonpolluting type (the average use life of present-day automobiles is seven years). The carrot and the stick are now both operative: each remaining combustion engine vehicle will pay a $100 "air use fee," while each electric car owner will still get a $100 "incentive bonus" for the year. Toward the end of the transitional decade, the "carrot" tends to become ineffective, but the "stick" will begin to hurt; so it can be expected that the motivation for changeover will remain, until the percentage of combustion-engine vehicles on the road is reduced to an inconsequential level.

Very simple: no rigid injunctions, no arbitrary deadline, no ineffective litigation in court. Instead, a gentle (but persistent and continuous) pressure for change operating within the system itself.

No cost to government: the economics of the device are contained in a closed system. All the money collected from the smog makers goes to the pioneer users of smog-free devices.

No unfair penalty to any particular group—unless it be the investors in oil production, but they will probably be the first to shift to investment in the manufacture of the new type of vehicles.

Obviously, the brief description is an oversimplification. The "air use fee" should not be a constant "per car" rate, but rather should be proportional to engine displacement (or, even better, be attached to the cost of gasoline. 2¢ per gallon would be, on the average, equivalent to the initial yearly fee of $20 per car).

Furthermore, it is probable that relatively old used cars should be, at least initially, exempted from the "use fee" to avoid penalizing the poor who may not be able to purchase the new type of vehicle, and thus would be unable to take advantage of the incentive bonus (though, as I indicated earlier, it might well be possible to finance entirely the new vehicles, at least during the early years, by means of the "incentive bonus").

The technique, I am ready to concede, would have to undergo scrutiny, modification and refinement. But the concept remains attractively unchallengeable: make the system correct itself! The side benefits are countless: relieved of dependency on oil, we could readily forego shoreline drilling (thus the reference to Santa Barbara at the beginning), and we could loosen certain uncomfortable ties with oil-producing potentates in the Middle East (thus the second reference vitiated as it might be by wishful thinking).

Indeed the "concept" could have unlimited applications. Any desirable device or development that produces undesirable side effects can be coaxed rather than coerced into reducing and eliminating the undesirable side effects by the "stick and carrot" method.

If industry on the Great Lakes is polluting the water, collect a "water use fee" proportional to volume and degree of contamination, and distribute the collected funds as bonuses to those industries that eliminate (or drastically reduce) contamination.

If DDT has undesirable side effects, no need to ban it. Simply discourage its use by collecting an "environment contamination" fee at the source; redistribute the accumulated funds to the users of new noncontaminating pest-control chemicals.

This, then, is the proposal in its simplest form. It should constitute an attractive alternative and a bold departure from the current policy of emission controls that is bound to generate unfulfillable expectations rather then positive achievement.

Edgardo Contini was born in Ferrara, Italy, in 1914, graduated in Civil Engineering *summa cum laude* from the University of Rome in 1937, and came to the United States in 1939. After service with the U.S. Army Corps of Engineers during World War II, he practiced as a consulting engineer in Los Angeles. In 1951 he became one of the founding partners of Gruen Associates, and in that capacity has been responsible for the direction of many of the major architectural and planning projects entrusted to the firm.

Mr. Contini's activities have included writing for publication in professional and educational journals, as well as lecturing and teaching at both UCLA and USC.

Mr. Contini's major role—both in the professional and the educational fields—has been the bridging of the gaps between engineering, architecture and planning. In the fulfillment of this role within the framework of a humanistic outlook, Mr. Contini's interests and crusades have ranged well beyond the rigid confines of professional specialization. An early adversary of "growth for growth's sake," an earnest advocate of national commitment to a rational policy of urban settlement, Mr. Contini has dealt with such diverse subjects as sabbaticals for all in an affluent society and involvement of the universities in urban affairs.

CHAPTER 8

Environment and the Law

Michael Kitzmiller

> . . . despite the very serious nature of the threat to
> environmental preservation, the inherent inertia of our
> system will probably block effective action at least
> until public concern is galvanized by some catastrophic
> disaster. We can only hope that such a disaster, when it
> does come, will not have taken us over the environ-
> mental threshold past the point of no return.

The mid-twentieth century marked an important turning point in the relationship between man and his environment. For the first time we came face to face with the fact that, unaided by plagues or natural disasters, man now has the potential to bring about the cataclysmic destruction, not only of civilization on this planet, but of life itself.

This potential was first brought home to us with the dawn of the nuclear era. Now, however, there is growing concern that the forces created by our exploding world population and our headlong technological development have placed man's finger upon an "environmental trigger," fully as real and fully as dangerous as the "nuclear trigger."

In fact, the danger may even be greater from the environmental trigger. A nuclear catastrophe involves a positive, deliberate action—a decision to destroy. The environmental trigger can be "pulled" by indifference, by our merely continuing to do the things we have always done in the same careless way.

Philosophically, man today is ill-equipped to come to grips with this new threat. One of the basic articles of faith of the conventional wisdom of the twentieth century is the belief in man's unique ability to apply technology to conquering "nature" and controlling his own environment. However, as Arnold Toynbee has noted, the real victory may turn out to have been for technology, not man; and we have a growing number of examples of unfortunate fruits of this victory.

1. The pesticides upon which we now depend to maintain certain parts of our food supply may so disturb the balance of our ecosystem as to threaten other equally important food sources, if not man himself;

2. The power industry upon which our economy depends so heavily threatens to strangle and poison us in its efforts to keep pace with demand;

3. The processes we have devised to deal with water pollution are themselves producing a new form of pollution which, in some circumstances, can be as deadly to our environment as the raw sewage the processes are designed to cleanse;

4. Even so mundane a matter as our transportation network may be attacking factors essential to the balance and function of our ecosystem.

On almost every hand we are faced with conflicts between preservation of a livable environment and technological development—conflicts that we are learning cannot be resolved merely by new technology.

In an effort to resolve these conflicts, concerned citizens have frequently turned to the law. In some cases, they have turned to the courts to apply and interpret existing law. In others, they have turned to legislative bodies for new protection. There have been some victories, and more defeats; but objective analysis of even the so-called victories would, I think, lead to the conclusion that existing legal mechanisms do not address themselves to the new and serious challenges we face and are not adequate to resolve them.

One basic fault is that our concept of law is rooted in the belief that man has the right, even a moral obligation to exploit natural resources. This legal philosophy, in turn, is founded upon the deeply-ingrained, if erroneous, belief that the resources of our environment are infinite; that we live at the open end of a natural horn of plenty. Of course, there are limitations on this concept. For example, when the exploitation would do direct, measurable injury to the property of another, or, as in the case of the Forestry legislation, when the competition between exploiters has become so intense that intervention is necessary to keep the exploiters from destroying not only an economically valuable resource, but themselves to boot. Even here, however, it is essential to note that the basic philosophy is that the environmental resources exist to be exploited; the only question is *how*—not *whether*.

A review of several typical efforts to apply legal mechanisms may help to show the way the present philosophic orientation and legal structure inhibit every effort to use the law to resolve the conflicts.

The Courts

The decision of the U.S. Court of Appeals for the Second Circuit in the *Storm King* case has been rightly hailed as one of the great modern conservation victories.

The case was born when one of the nation's largest public utilities, Consolidated Edison of New York, proposed to build a pumped storage power generating plant on Storm King Mountain, the northern gateway to the Hudson Highlands. After perfunctory hearings, the Federal Power Commission (FPC) licensed the plant in spite of strong opposition from conservation groups and citizens. The major opposition, Scenic Hudson Preservation Conference, sued to have the license revoked. The United States Court of Appeals for the Second Circuit agreed with the opponents and remanded the license to the FPC for further hearings, finding that the Commission had failed to develop a complete record on a variety of issues, including, ". . . among other things, cost, public convenience, and the absence of reasonable alternatives". (354 F.2d 608)

Aside from the temporary victory of blocking the construction of the plant, the decision established two important precedents. Most important, the Court held that under the Federal Power Act citizen groups had standing to challenge projects that might have an adverse impact on the environment, even though they sustained no direct, economic injury. The essential element was the demonstration of a genuine concern for the environmental factors involved. This concept has since been considerably expanded in decisions on other cases.

The decision also defined the responsibility of federal agencies to develop, of their own motion, information concerning the impact that a project under their jurisdiction might have on the environment, warning that such agencies could no longer ". . . act as an umpire, blandly calling balls and strikes for adversaries appearing before it . . . ."

These precedents have already played an important role in other legal cases such as the *Mineral King* case and the *Hudson River Expressway* case, and they should have a profound effect upon the way in which Federal agencies treat environmental matters in future deliberations.*

But this important conservation victory reveals serious flaws in the system.

As a practical matter, the cost to the scenic Hudson of the six-year battle—perhaps in excess of half a million dollars, which had to be raised

---

* In fact, the impact of the Storm King case has not been limited to environmental issues. It has had a profound influence on other types of cases involving the citizens right to participate in governmental decisions, most notably United Church of Christ vs FCC (354 F.2d 494). In this case, the present Chief Justice of the U.S. Supreme Court, then serving on the U.S. Court of Appeals, followed the precedent in overturning a decision of the FCC. The FCC had ruled that a group of black citizens in Jackson, Mississippi, did not have the standing to challenge a television license, merely because the station failed to represent their interests adequately.

The court disagreed. In fact, it had to disagree twice, because the FCC committed the same error in rehearing the case after the first rebuff. The first time, the court set the case back to the FCC for further hearing. The second time it flatly reversed the FCC decision, convinced that the agency either couldn't or wouldn't do its job properly.

from the general public—clearly exceeds the resources normally available to the average group. Had the true cost of the superb legal talent been paid, the figure would have been several times greater. Not only is this kind of funding generally out of the reach of citizen's groups, but there is serious ethical question as to whether the general public should be put to the expense at all. A good case could be made as to the impropriety of requiring the public to "buy again" environmental assets which seem to be public property in the first place.

The greatest deficiency, however, was that the Court's decision never resolved, nor even addressed, the central issue involved in the *Storm King* case and in almost every other environmental conflict. On the one hand there is a continually growing public demand for more of the benefits of technology which require the exploitation of more and more of our environmental assets, whether they be land, water, air or less tangible assets such as beauty and tranquility. Set against this is the desperate need to preserve and enhance these resources, which are dwindling under constant assault not only from power generation, but from a host of other technological developments as well. The central problem is how to weigh the conflicting demands in a context that will produce rational and usable answers.

In making the decision whether to permit the construction of a power project, the FPC compares the cost of the project against the benefits to be derived. Heretofore, costs and benefits have been considered in economic and technological terms only. Under the impact of the *Storm King* decision, it is now recognized that the Commission (and presumably, by extension, other agencies as well) must also consider environmental factors. But the Commission has never developed a formula for evaluating these environmental factors so that they can be meaningfully included in this cost-benefit consideration, and no court has yet required them to do so. In the absence of such a formula, it would appear that under the Federal Power Act, and, in fact, all other laws affecting the exploitation of resources, environmental factors can never be considered in the same decision-making context with economy and technology. Perhaps in some future battle, the requirement that projects with environmental consequences serve the "public convenience and necessity" could be expanded to include a consideration of total costs (if such a formula is possible). However, experience in the *Storm King* case indicates that establishing such a precedent might well be costly, time-consuming, and unsure.

It should also be pointed out that, nothwithstanding the expense and time invested, the *Storm King* case resolved nothing. It merely deferred decision. The court, reluctant to substitute judicial decision for the findings of a federal commission, would not, and perhaps could not, make the final judgment as to whether environmental issues outweighed power issues. Instead, in what most predicted would be a futile gesture of faith in the regulatory system, the court remanded the case to the same agency which had already more than demonstrated its lack of ability and even greater lack of interest in dealing with environmental issues.

The decision was handed down on December 28, 1965, two years after the controversy had started. But the weary, stale and unprofitable business continued. In November, 1966, the FPC held the first of what later stretched to some 80 days of hearings in the reopened procedure. For month upon month, and even year upon year, concerned citizens appeared before the hearing examiner, raising issues, questioning premises and struggling vainly to find some hope that the Commission had heard the Court and understood its message.

As a result of the Court's decision the Commission with obvious reluctance, did give a greater consideration to environmental matters; greater at least in the sense that examiners received evidence that they had earlier refused even to hear. (The Commission's discomfort was best illustrated in the outburst of an FPC lawyer during the examination of a Con Edison witness by a lawyer for the Sierra Club. The FPC attorney interrupted questioning as to the way the Company's representatives considered and evaluated scenic assets. The Commission's lawyer complained that he was amazed that utilities had the "temerity" to come down here and ask for projects when they face opposition like this. Since up to this time only two out of about 1500 major industry applications had been rejected by the FPC,—and only one of those, the Namakegon project, on what might be described in any was as an environmental consideration—the "temerity" of utilities might more accurately be described as "confidence".

On December 23, 1969, the opponents' expectations were realized when the examiner issued a decision supporting the *Storm King* project, and seven months later, following a brief oral argument, the Commission ratified the examiner's findings and reissued Con Edison's license.

A review of the opinion points up clearly the basic flaws in the system. *Longer* consideration is in no way equivalent to *better* consideration. The Commission had given consideration to environmental issues by receiving evidence, but having no idea what to do with it, and no procedure for handling it, simply ignored it. The determinations were still made by the technicians whose principal responsibility, as well as experience and personal predisposition lie in the development of power resources, not parks. The decision was made pursuant to the requirements and underlying philosophy of the Federal Power Act which was never designed to protect the environment—nor really, in fact, to consider it—but, explicitly, to promote hydro-power development in the United States. The whole proceeding is as inherently unfair as it would be to compel the utilities to come before a board made up of dedicated conservationists for permission to build a plant.

The result then, was inevitable, for the Commission is committed to the development of power. It can try to minimize damage, but it is not equipped to address itself to the more fundamental issues raised by Justice William O. Douglas in the *High Mountain Sheep* case: Ought the project to be built at all?

Faced with the grim certainty of having to reappear before a federal court that had already expressed its strong disapproval of the Commission's behavior in the case, FPC officials went out of their way to create the *appearance* of considering the disputed questions, but there their interest predictably stopped.

The case is now again before the Second Circuit Court. There is no way of guessing the outcome. There is a slight possibility that even now, after eight years of contention, the ultimate decision may still be deferred.

The *Storm King* "victory" points up some of the inadequacies of our existing court mechanisms for resolving environmental conflicts, but also clearly shows that the flaw goes much deeper into our system of laws.

Legislation

The vast body of existing law—constitutional, common and statute—is almost all oriented towards exploitation of resources; conservation, when considered at all, is traditionally treated as a quaint form of husbandry designed to assure a continuing supply of natural resources for exploitation. The law is not geared to consider the consequences that may result within a finite system from the exhaustion of environmental assets. Sporadic legislative efforts to correct these deficiencies built into the system have not been successful.

The Fish and Wildlife Coordination Act, (P.L. 85-624), which represents the very best of this type of effort, declared it to be the policy of Congress to recognize:

> . . . the vital contributions of our wildlife resources to the Nation . . .
> and to provide that wildlife conservation shall receive equal consideration
> and be coordinated with other features of water-resource development
> programs . . . (16 U.S.C. 661).

The act directed all agencies and departments of the federal government to consult with the U.S. Fish and Wildlife Service "with a view to the conservation of wildlife resources by preventing loss of and damage to such resources . . ." (16 U.S.C. 662[a]), and it authorized the U.S. Fish and Wildlife Service to make necessary studies and investigations to carry out the declared policies of the act.

Hearings before the Fisheries and Wildlife Subcommittee of the House Merchant Marine and Fisheries Committee, in 1969, on the controversial Hudson River Expressway showed the utter ineffectuality of this blanket legal mechanism as a means of protecting even such well-recognized environmental assets as commercial and sports fish.

The *Hudson River Expressway* case involves a proposal by the New York State Department of Transportation to construct a six-lane commercial expressway, 3.6 miles of which are to be built actually in the bed of the Hudson River itself. The proposal first surfaced in 1965, at which time it was clear that the permit authority of the U.S. Army Corps of Engineers would be involved and that the U.S. Department of the Interior would be obliged to pass on that permit with a view toward protecting all natural resources of the river, and, specifically, its fish resources.

As proposed, the construction would involve dredging 3.2-million cubic yards of unsuitable material from the bed of the Hudson and replacing it with 9.5-million cubic yards of fill material to support the road bed. The construction would extend up to 1,300 feet into the river and would destroy between 350 and 450 acres of valuable wetlands and shoal in what has been described as the most valuable tidal estuary on the Atlantic seaboard.

Among the 48 species of fish that depend upon the area are many anadromous fish, including the striped bass and several varieties of sturgeon, one of which has been officially declared an "endangered species" by the Department of the Interior.

In a general study of the riverway conducted in 1966, the Interior Department itself noted the great significance of the Hudson as a fishery resource. It further asserted that the shoals play a vital role in supporting the young of anadromous fish as they work their way towards the sea. Without the shoal these fish could not survive. Perhaps most surprisingly, the report stressed that there was no reliable information on the ecology of the river; that it was vital that studies be conducted to find ways to preserve and enhance the fish resources which it described even then, as threatened by technological development affecting the riverway.

In spite of this knowledge, in spite of clear warning from a state-employed biologist that the consequences of construction of the expressway could be serious, adverse, and perhaps permanent, and, finally, in spite of its clear statutory responsibility under the Fish and Wildlife Coordination Act, the Interior Department never made or proposed studies either of the marine resources or of the impact of the proposed expressway upon them.

During the congressional hearings into the matter this year, it was revealed that the Interior Department did absolutely nothing for three and one-half years. Then, in 1968, when the Corps' application for a permit was forwarded to Interior for comment, the department officials determined that there was not adequate time to make the necessary "studies and investigations." Instead, they relied upon "available data," assembled by the state and consisting mostly of limited studies of fishery resources made in 1937. Based solely upon this information, Interior issued a statement saying that it had no objection to the project. In fact it was revealed later that the then-Secretary of the Interior, Stewart L. Udall, had made up his mind to approve the construction at least a month before even the meager information from the "available data" had been made available.

The committee was appalled at the impotence of the congressional mandate. However, they should not have been. The same philosophy that shaped the FPC underlies the organic law of the U.S. Army Corps of Engineers and the Interior Department. Each agency was established with the purpose of achieving maximum exploitation and development of the resources over which it was given jurisdiction. It ought, therefore, to come as no shock to learn that their basic attitude in considering a project is not "should the project be built?" but when it is built, "how can we obtain the maximum (dollar) benefit from it?"*

---

*On July 11, 1969, the U.S. District Court for the Southern District of New York killed the Hudson River Expressway proposal and this decision was later upheld by the U.S. Court of Appeals for the Second Circuit. The most significant thing about the victory, however, is that it did *not* come about upon the environmental issue. It was based upon a legal technicality. The State's proposal called for the use of dikes in the construction of that portion of the Expressway that was to be built in the Hudson. The engineering drawings showed the structures as dikes and even described them as "dikes" in the specifications. Until 1966, when Congress enacted the Department of Transportation Act (49 U.S.C. 1651) there was considerable confusion of authority regarding the construction of bridges, causeways, dikes and the like. In the 1966 Act, Congress moved to coordinate all this authority under the Secretary of Transportation and thus eliminate duplictory and unnecessarily cumbersome procedures. One thing, however, that it did not include in this new procedure, was dikes. Under the prevailing law first enacted in 1899 (33 U.S.C. 401), only Congress can authorize the construction of dikes in navigable waters. This provision was not changed by the Department of Transportation Act or any other measure. The Corps, the State of New York and the Department of Transportation all argued that this was merely an oversight and that Congress hadn't known what it was doing at the time. In this view, they are supported by some distinguished lawyers, notably the environmental attorney, Professor Joseph Sax (Defending The Environment: A strategy for Citizen Action, Alfred A. Knopf, New York, 1971). The Court apparently, and I think quite properly, dismissed this as presumptous, preferring in the absence of compelling evidence to the contrary to believe that Congress did know what it was doing and did what it intended. I would point out that if Congress didn't know what it was doing, it could easily remedy the error by approving the dikes for the expressway and changing the law, something it has shown no inclination even to consider.

Regardless of whether Congress knew what it was doing or not, the fact remains that the issue was decided upon a technicality of law and procedure. The Court never once directly addressed the central issue: would the proposed Expressway damage the environment in such a serious way as to outweigh its claimed benefits for transportation?

The ecologists involved in this battle who had, to man, satisfied themselves that the Expressway would have been ruinously destructive, heaved a sigh of relief that this was not the central issue before the court. In spite of the overwhelming evidence, they would have lost because there is no legal mechanism for considering that aspect of the project.

It is, in short, inevitable that policies such as that so well expressed in the Fish and Wildlife Coordination Act will always be subverted by the basic orientation of the agencies charged with implementation.

This same flaw mars most of our efforts to legislate environmental quality. Experience shows that even ambitious legislative packages such as the Clean Waters Restoration Act and the Air Quality Control Act simply cannot achieve their goals, given the built-in exceptions and delays designed to protect the exploiters.

Another crucial flaw common to past legislative and court efforts to resolve environmental conflicts has been the tendency to deal with them on a piecemeal, case-by-case basis. We fight an individual legal battle to save one mountain, another to preserve one estuary; we draft separate laws to protect one resource, such as fish and wildlife, and another law to fight air pollution. This approach may have been adequate in the past for conservation battles dealing with the more tangible, natural assets, but it cannot meet the more fundamental challenge that we face in the near future.

The most serious technological threats to our environment do not come from individual assaults from any one source, but from the cumulative effect of broad assaults from many sides. Thus, for example, while there may be a legitimate question as to the wisdom of a specific location chosen for a particular nuclear plant, the more serious question is what the effect of a group of nuclear plants within any part of our ecosystem may be, and, further, the extent to which this effect, taken in conjunction with other environmental assaults, may stress these environmental assets beyond endurance.

A mechanism to review and effectively control the impact of these broad assaults is desperately needed. This is true not only for the new developments but also for such long-established fruits of technology such as our national transportation system. The average American views highways as either a convenience or a nuisance, depending upon whether he passes over them or they pass over him, but the environmental consequences of our growing national transportation network may be far more significant than either its advantages or its nuisance value.

Because so much of our emphasis has been on highway construction and not on alternative methods of transportation, we find ourselves caught in a vicious cycle. The more highways we build, the more we rely on cars, trucks, and buses. In turn, the more we rely on cars, trucks and buses, the more highways we need to keep pace with our growing demand.

The most obvious immediate product of this situation has been the dramatic increase in the number of "freeway fights," such as those in New York City, Washington, D.C., New Orleans, and a growing number of cities around the country. Citizens who object to having their homes and communities paved over, raise legitimate environmental issues which past experience shows they will have to fight in the courts on a case-by-case basis—and usually lose.

But there are broader environmental implications which cannot be fought now because no appropriate forum exists.

The health of citizens in many of our cities is already threatened with pollution caused by the internal combustion engine which, nationally, is said to account for two-thirds of the poison we dump into the air. Even the most optimistic view of the effectiveness of today's abatement methods indicates that we would barely manage to maintain a health *status quo* if we stopped growing right now, which we are not likely to do. It will not be until the problem becomes so acute that it poses direct, measurable injury to large numbers of individuals that it would be possible to bring the matter to the courts or to effectively seek legislation. In California and in New York City this time may well be near. But to attack the problem on an individual case basis still is to avoid facing the fundamental issues.

There is at least one other serious environmental problem raised by highways which has not received any attention whatever: the very serious impact they may have upon our water resources.

An important source of fresh water is the aquifer, the underground supply that is replenished largely by rain seeping into the ground. This resource is jeopardized because an increasing amount of rain falls on highways, pavements or other run-off areas where it is collected in sewers and carried directly into streams and rivers to be lost forever in the oceans. Major U.S. highways alone have been estimated to divert as much as 335 *billion* gallons of water a year and the highways that will be built by the year 2000 will add another 1.5 *trillion* a year.

Viewed in light of the Water Resources Council's predictions in its report to President Johnson, this problem takes on new long-range significance. The Council warned that by the year 2010 the demand for fresh water will match the total available national supply. We will then be able to expand our resources only by a massive conservation effort, by desalination, and by recycling and reuse.

There are probably other adverse effects that our highways program has upon the environment, but these few are sufficient to indicate our urgent need of some way of taking a broad overview of the fruits of each and all of our technological developments.

Proposals

The combined forces of the growing public concern over the seriousness of environmental conflicts and awareness of the inadequacy of existing mechanisms for resolving them have generated a large number of legislative proposals for corrective action. So great has been the public demand, in fact, that several proposals have actually been filtered through our cumbersome legislative process and been enacted into law.* Experience to date indicates that none of the laws or proposals provide satisfactory answers. They do, however, serve to underscore some of the basic problems and indicate directions that need further exploration.

The Environmental Council

One of the earliest and most persistent proposals called for the creation of a new agency to serve as watchdog and counselor to the executive in environmental matters. The form of the agency and the extent of its powers vary widely from proposal to proposal. At one end of the spectrum is the independent body with staff to conduct its own studies and evaluations and authority to intervene to block or modify programs that it finds environmentally damaging. At the weakest end of the spectrum is the council with only advisory and study powers. This latter concept was embodied in law in the Environmental Policy Act of 1969.**

With all its weaknesses, and they are many, the Environmental Policy Act cannot be dismissed out of hand as worthless. It did mark an important first step. It represented the first Congressional effort to establish and implement a broad national policy on environmental matters. If it is ambivalent and even vaguely schizoid,† this perhaps again reflects the deeper cultural ambivalence that we must come to grips with if we are to shape an effective policy. This is evident in the very statement of the policy in the Act itself. The statement speaks of attaining the "widest range of beneficial uses of the environment". It calls for maintaining, "wherever possible, an environment which supports diversity and variety of individual choice". Perhaps most significantly, it seeks to "achieve a

---

*Action has by no means been limited to the Federal legislature. Some of the most interesting and effective proposals have come from state and local bodies. For example, Michigan has led the nation in adopting the Environmental Protection Act of 1970, which, among other things permits the bringing of class actions in environmental matters and, once the plaintiff has shown that he has a *prima facia* case as to the existence of a problem, shifts the burden of proof to the defendant to show that his action is "consistent with promotion of the public health, safety and welfare in light of the state's paramount condern for the protection of its natural resources from pollution, impairment or destruction". (Enrolled House Bill 3055.) Equally significant are the local actions such as that the County Council of Montgomery County, Maryland,which has banned the sale of disposable bottles and the respresentatives of Suffolk County, New York, who have banned the sale of detergents.

**PL 91-190 signed into law by President Nixon on January 1, 1970.

†Not all the ambiguity of the Act can be blamed on our national failures. A good deal of the confusion comes from the fact that its final form was the end product of truly titanic confrontation between two of the most dogmatic and powerful egos of Congress, Senator Henry M. Jackson and Senator Edward S. Muskie, both of whom were competing for the title of "Mr. Environment" and, more importantly, for jurisdiction over the Council created by the Act. Since neither could honestly be characterized as an environmentalist, the basic goal—environmental protection—occasionally got lost in the process.

balance between population and resource use which will permit high standards of living and a wide sharing of life's amenities". In short, its otherwise unexceptionable purposes are limited by the same man-oriented, exploitive philosophies that taint our existing law. Even assuming the best intentions possible, the administrator faced with implementing the policy set forth in the Act will repeatedly find himself faced with conflicts between present amenities and future survival; conflicts which he has no help in resolving since the guidelines in the Act are in conflict themselves. Since nothing has been done to offset the overshelming dominance of the exploitive interests, the outcome of such conflicts will only be in doubt when a large national constituency can be mobilized against a specific exploitation as in the Everglades Jetport case.

The Act *does* direct federal agencies to fully explore and fairly weigh environmental considerations in carrying out their statutory responsibilities, but it then makes it clear that these considerations are not to be construed as interfering with the existing statutory responsibilities of the agency. In essence, therefore, the Act would seem to tell an agency like the Federal Power Commission: weigh environmental evidence, and then go ahead and do what you were told to do when you were created (e.g., license power dams) unless there is overwhelming evidence that a given project will permanently damage the environment.

Finally, the Act set up a Council on Environmental Quality which is to oversee the way in which Federal agencies carry out their new responsibilities. When all is said and done, this Council has only two duties. It reviews federal programs and proposals to determine the extent to which they are consistent with environmental preservation and it prepares reports for the President on the environmental impact of certain federal projects, after having evaluated reports received from other concerned federal agencies. The significance of this later responsibility has been badly overestimated by conservationists. You have only to remember the performance of the Interior Department in discharging its statutory responsibilities in the Hudson River Expressway case to understand the weakness of this type of protection. If you have a council made up of people devoted to their environmental responsibilities and impervious to political and economic pressures, and if they are supported by the President and a Congress equally devoted and independent, it might work—*if* the environmental information supplied by the other agencies were full, accurate and unbiased.

The way in which the Council discharges its responsibility to report on the environmental impact of federal programs illustrates a grave weakness in the approach. The Act requires that the environmental reports be public. The present chairman, Russell Train, has interpreted the Council's responsibility as extending only to releasing its own reports. He relies upon other agencies to release theirs, if they so desire.

Furthermore, he has so far not released the data upon which such reports are based. Perhaps most serious is the question of timing. If the reports are to be of any use at all, they must be released in time to be studied and evaluated by the decision makers. In one case a key report on proposals incorporated in the Rivers and Harbors bill was released only after the bill had almost worked its way through Congress. This kind of effort can not be expected to contribute much to meaningful discussions of important and complex issues. Since the concerned public (and in some cases even the legislature) is deprived of any way of evaluating the data upon which the Council's recommendations are based, it has no alternative but to rely upon the supposed expertise of the Council, a very chancy business indeed. If the Council were expert, wholly honest, devoted to the environment and completely independent of any pressure, the system might work; but that is the only way.

At its best, the Council does provide a new, centralized forum for the review of environmental conflicts. At its worst, it is only one more inaccessible governmental body unaccountable to the public for its decisions.

In less than two years of existence, the Council on Environmental Policy and the Act that created it have chalked up a rather impressive record of failure. The important question, however, is could it succeed? Are the failures inherent in the concept or merely the result of defects in the execution?

The mechanical flaws—the failure to conduct or publicize meaningful studies of specific projects—can be easily mended by new legislation. The ambivalence about environment is another matter. To look to legislation or even administration to resolve this in the absence of a clear public decision is clearly hopeless.

It is important to remember, however, that any agency deriving its muscle from the President, as the Council does, is wholly dependent upon the incumbent for the success of its mission. If the President is a sincere and single-minded environmentalist, the agency will succeed. If he is a practical politician who builds his constituency from compromise and accomodation, the agency will be compelled to mirror this approach in its actions. Any observer who has charted the shifting fortunes of such executive agencies as the Office of Science and Technology, the Commission on Violence or even the Interior Department under the direction of Stewart Udall, has good reason to be dubious of the prospects for success of any new agency that derives its impetus from the Office of the President—any President.

Two other actions have taken place which are harder to evaluate at this point. First Congress, over President Nixon's strong objections, created an Office of Environmental Quality in the Office of the President. Aside from its value of giving Senator Jackson one in the nose from Senator Muskie, the purpose of this Act is not very clear. Many think that its main utility is to provide more funding for projects of the Council on Environmental Quality. Since President Nixon, who is supposed to be served by the Office of Environmental Quality, has described its enactment as "a mistake",* it seems unlikely that the Office will be put to constructive use in this Administration.

The second action is more interesting. On July 9, 1970, the President under his authority to reorganize the executive agencies** created in a new Environmental Protection Agency into which he coordinated many of the environmental responsibilities of other existing agencies, such as, for example, the Federal Water Quality Administration, which was formerly in Interior, and the Environmental Health Service which had been in HEW. Again, it is much too early to evaluate this new agency's performance, although it can be noted that it has apparently already lost its first important battle in its conflict with the Atomic Energy Commission over the control of radiation standards.

Nor would the problem be resolved by turning to the legislative branch as several bills presently before Congress would provide. Again, there is considerable variation in the structure and authority proposed. One would create a Joint Congressional Committee on the Environment. Another would create an organization similar to the Government Accounting Office, an agency wholly independent of the executive and responsible only to Congress.

The problem with all of these proposals is that their effectiveness would be no greater than congressional concern. Furthermore, the traditional jealousy between congressional committees which so marred the Environmental Protection Act, would make it impractical, if not impossible, for such a group to exercise broad oversight responsibilities. The highway program, for example, is the private preserve of the Public Works Committee. No other committee could, or would attempt to, interject itself into considerations affecting highways. It would take a broader reorganization of Congress than anyone presently envisages to persuade the existing committees to give up their extremely powerful prerogatives.

The Environmental Council as a Quasi-Judicial Agency

Legislation has been proposed that would establish an independent, quasi-judicial agency patterned after the Federal Power Commission (FPC) and the Federal Communications Commission (FCC) and

*Statement by the President upon signing bill establishing the Council on Environmental Quality. January 1, 1970, Federal Register, Monday, January 5, 1970, page 11.

**Reorganization Plan 3 of 1970 under the authority of Chapter 9, title 5 of the U.S. Code.

empowered to intervene in any federal action when it deems that the action might adversely affect environmental assets.*

On the surface, this is an extremely attractive idea. It would create a flexible forum in which to air broad environmental issues and an effec-effective source of authority for enforcing environmental protection.

As a practical matter, however, those who are familiar with the operation of the FPC, the FCC and similar regulatory agencies may be justifiably dubious. Experience bears out John Kenneth Galbraith's observation that "regulatory agencies like the people who comprise them, have a marked life cycle. In youth, they are vigorous, aggressive, evangelistic and even tolerant. Later they mellow, and in old age—after a matter of ten or fifteen years—they become either the arm of the industry they are regulating or senile." What he did not point out was that once an agency is established and its arteries have hardened, getting rid of it is virtually impossible.

Whether it is possible to create a regulatory agency that will be able to maintain the youthful and vigorous approach that is needed to deal with environmental concerns is problematical. Certainly no such agency should be created lightly.

Legislation

The failure of the past legislative efforts does not warrant dismissing consideration of this approach as a possible solution. It has been suggested, for example, that a broad law might be enacted setting forth a new policy of Congress that no action will be permitted which will have unreasonably adverse effect upon environmental assets and giving the courts authority to enjoin such actions. To mitigate the problem of excessive costs of such legal actions, this act might provide funds which could be made available to support any action in which the court finds colorable controversy.

Obviously, such a statute would not be easy to frame, and the potential areas of conflict with existing law are substantial. Carefully drafted, it might be an effective tool, especially if it went hand in hand with the creation of a national agency with broad oversight powers.

In the 91st Congress, a first, if somewhat tentative, step was made in this direction. When the Airport and Airway Development Act of 1970 came before Congress, there was a great deal of concern over the possible environmental impact of projects constructed under its $5 billion authorization. Experience with the ill-conceived Everglades Jetport proposal and with proposals for the extension of New York's John Fitz-

*One excellent version of this proposal was incorporated in H.R. 7052 in the 91st Congress. In this case the authority of the Council was limited to projects and proposals under the jurisdiction of the Federal Power Commission.

gerald Kennedy Airport into Jamaica Bay, intensified the grave doubts that had already been raised—and largely confirmed—by experience with noise congestion and pollution from New York's LaGuardia and Washington's National Airports. When the bill was under consideration by the House Commerce Committee, then-Representative Richard L. Ottinger (D-N.Y.) offered the following amendment which was adopted over stiff opposition:*

> (4) It is declared to be national policy that airport development projects authorized pursuant to this part shall provide for the protection and enhancement of the natural resources and the quality of environment of the Nation. In implementing this policy, the Secretary shall consult with the secretaries of the Interior and Health, Education, and Welfare with regard to the effect that any project involving airport location, a major runway extension, or runway location may have on natural resources including, but not limited to, fish and wildlife, natural, scenic and recreation assets, water and air quality, and other factors affecting the environment, and shall authorize no such project found to have adverse effect unless the Secretary shall render a finding, in writing, following a full and complete review, which shall be a matter of public record, that no feasible and prudent alternative exists and that all possible steps have been taken to minimize such adverse effect.

With the skilled support of Michigan's Senator Philip A. Hart, the amendment survived Senate action and is now law.**

The real strength of this provision lies in its simplicity. It sets a clear standard which a court can apply should citizens protest an airport proposal. It is not circumscribed or clouded by weakening escape clauses such as "in so far as possible" or "insofar as is consistent with other objectives". It is clear, simple and succint.

Furthermore, it does not allow Federal authority to hide behind the smoke screen of "administrative expertise" or unpublished "expert studies and findings". The Secretary of Transportation has an affirmative responsibility to make a finding and make public the evidence to support that finding. The amendment has yet to be tested in Court, perhaps because its purpose and effect are so clear that affected officials are observing its intent, or more probably, because their plans have not advanced to the stage where they would be subject to review.

If such provisions were to be made a part of each new authorization, it would be a great forward stride for environmental sanity. However, it is important to remember that Congress handles literally thousands of bills each year. The 91st Congress alone considered 28,000 of which it passed 941. Of these, only perhaps 400 to 500 deal with issues which have some environmental impact, but that still means that environmen-

---

*84 STAT. 227 (c) (4)
**(PL 91-258)

talists might have to fight 200 to 500 individual battles each year to win effective environmental protection. This has all the flaws that have been found in striving for environmental protections through legal actions and has one other fault that is even graver. The exploitive interests represent a large and effective lobby to which Congress is extremely receptive. There is some question as to whether the Ottinger airport amendment would have survived this lobby's assault in the Senate had there not been a bitter controversy over a proposal to extend a major airport facility into the Columbia River. A large number of the citizens of the State of Washington were incensed over the Columbia proposal, and made their feeling clearly known to their congressional representatives, including Senator Warren G. Magnuson. Senator Magnuson is the powerful chairman of the Senate Commerce Committee which had jurisdiction over the Airport Bill. We cannot rely upon such fortuitous and determinative circumstances in most situations.

Finally, there is a common flaw in all efforts to deal with environmental conflicts through legislation in the absence of a real reordering of our national commitment. What is enacted by statute can be changed by statute; Congress proposes and disposes and what Congress has proposed it can just as easily dispose of.

The Three Sisters Bridge controversy in Washington, D.C. is perhaps the best example. The Bridge and its related Freeway would destroy not only a considerable scenic asset in the Potomac River, but a substantial section of the black community of Washington as well. The proposal is, and has been for several years, opposed by virtually every citizens group in the District of Columbia, by the authorities of nearby Maryland and by almost every politician in the greater Washington area. Poll after poll has shown that it has no substantial support in any affected community. On the other side of the controversy, the bridge is warmly supported by the highway lobby and by their congressional representatives, William H. Natcher (D-Ky), who is the powerful chairman of the Subcommittee on the District of Columbia of the House Appropriations Committee and John C. Kluczynski (D-Ill), chairman of the Subcommittee on Roads of the House Public Works Committee.

Theoretically, it should have been no contest. Congress acted to create a permanent mechanism for resolving just this type of conflict four years ago when it adopted the Transportation Act of 1966.* The Act created standards and procedures to assure that future highway planning, design and construction would involve the community affected and would be consistent both with community wishes and environmental protection. Its clear and simple standards would admittedly have ruled out the Three Sisters Bridge without any further question. Nothing

*49 U.S.C. 1651-56

daunted, the Congressional Highwaymen neatly circumvented this by inserting in a provision in the 1968 Highway appropriation bill* which authorized the construction of the Three Sisters Bridge "notwithstanding any other provision of law". So much for legislating protection.

Adding strong environmental protection to individual legislative proposals is highly desirable, but it clearly cannot be relied upon as the only, or even the major, effort.

Constitutional Amendment

Perhaps the most intriguing proposal has been to amend the Constitution with a new section guaranteeing each citizen the protection of his environmental rights.

Such a provision of the Constitution would have been meaningless to those attending the Constitutional Convention in Philadelphia two hundred years ago. Indeed, even ten or twenty years ago it would have seemed quite unnecessary, although the handwriting was already on the wall for those with the vision to read it.

But today each of us has a fixed interest in all of our remaining natural resources and this interest is as significant a right as any guaranteed by our Constitution.

By declaring this as a matter of constitutional principle we are providing the most effective single protection within our power.

Any action which would impair the individual's interest in such essentials as clean air or fresh water or any of the other vital resources would be against express national policy and could be challenged in court as an assault upon our basic rights.

The tremendous educational campaign required to drum up the support necessary to win adoption of such an amendment is a drawback, and it probably is not within reach at the present time. However, this does not mean it should be dismissed out of hand as a long-range goal.

Conclusions

The sad fact is that despite the very serious nature of the threat to environmental preservation, the inherent inertia of our system will probably block effective action at least until public concern is galvanized by some catastrophic disaster. We can only hope that such a disaster, when it does come, will not have taken us over the environmental threshold past the point of no return.

Whatever we may want to believe, survival is not assured. It is a sobering reminder to reflect that of all the forms of life that have existed

*Federal-Aid Highway Act of 1968—82 STAT. 827; 23 (a)

upon this earth, 99 percent are now extinct and, to take literary license with the imperatives of evolutionary theory, they were trying to survive. Man, alone of all the species, is the only one with the capacity to exercise a measure of control over his environment; yet, as Dr. Ernst Mayr, Director of the Harvard Museum of Comparative Zoology has noted, "Almost everything we do is harmful to the species and works against our survival."

> *Extract from a letter of August 28, 1969 from Mr. Kitzmiller to Harvey Wheeler, Senior Fellow of the Center for the Study of Democratic Institutions. The references in the first paragraph are to the Center "Conference on the Constitutionalization of Science: Ethical and Philosophical Aspects of Biology," held on August 18-22, 1969.*

An observation made by Dr. Rotenstreich during a Friday session raised a question in my mind which I think demands greater attention. In answer to a statement by Michael Seriven concerning the role of education in preparing individuals to meet the demands of a technological revolution, Dr. Rotenstreich observed that even though people may be fully aware of threats to their survival and have the tools with which to meet them, there is no assurance that they will elect to use them. In effect, I believe he was saying that, faced with the conflict between preserving present amenities and preventing future catastrophe, a culture such as ours may knowingly opt for the amenities. If this is true—and I feel sure that is is—the implications are fully as staggering as those of the biological revolution.

I suspect that all of us have seen such a choice made in a small way. I once had a friend who, while relatively young (in his 50's), learned that he had both diabetes and a heart condition. By following a very stringent regimen, including a ghastly diet, he could reasonably have expected to extend his life span to a near normal point. By failing to observe the regimen, he knew that he would limit it to a matter of a few years.

I and his other friends, were quite impressed when he cheerfully chose to continue his accustomed life style and accept an early death. No one can honestly say how he felt at the end, but I can say that to all outward appearances, he had no regrets. I remember that there was much discussion among his friends of his courage and a general approval of the course he had chosen.

The significance of this is not the moral evaluation we made of his decision, which is truly irrelevant, but that here we have a perfect example of an intelligent, perceptive individual knowingly choosing the present amenities over future survival and of that choice being approved by the society within which he lived. Had he had some unfinished life's work, some unattained goal of great personal importance, I suspect he might well have chosen survival. However, he either had no such goal or, in his own mind, had achieved it, so that he opted for the present amenities instead.

In my time we have seen the same type of course followed by at least one nation: in the decline of the British empire. It is possible, even probable, that the end result would have been the same on a longer time scale; but it would appear that the immergence of the lower and lower-middle classes as a political power in England hastened the decline by reseting the national priorities towards improvement and maintenance of domestic conditions as against the expansion or even maintenance of the empire.

It is possible that we, in this country, have arrived at a similar decision? If the goal of our Constitution was to create a true middle-class society, and if we have, in effect, achieved that goal, will we choose the preservation of the existing structure, even though it may be clear to us that the result can only produce environmental conflicts that will surely be catastrophic? Is it possible that we may have reached such a level of "cultural" gratification that continuance of that gratification is really more important than the radical revisions that might be required for our society, and perhaps our species, to survive?

Wm. Michael Kitzmiller is Executive Director of Grassroots Action, Inc., a national citizen action group, and Vice President of the Environmental Clearinghouse, Inc., of Washington, D.C.

As Legislative Assistant to Congressman Richard L. Ottinger of New York, he wrote and guided to enactment the first Federal law designed to deal with problems of an urban river, the Hudson River Compact Act. He also authored the first legislation to deal with the problem of power transmission lines and legislation encouraging the development of a non-polluting alternative to the internal combustion engines. In 1968, he served as Special Assistant to Vice President Hubert H. Humphrey.

In 1963, Mr. Kitzmiller joined with a group of concerned citizens and conservationists in New York to oppose the plans of the Consolidated Edison Company of New York to build a pumped storage power plant on Storm King Mountain, which resulted in the historic Storm King Mountain decision. He has been active in a number of conservation issues involving Federal agencies ranging from the Grand Canyon battle to the Hudson River Expressway case and spearheaded the first Congressional investigation into the thermal fishkills from an atomic power plant, as well as investigations into abuses of transmission line right-of-way condemnation powers by utilities, violations of the Fish and Wildlife Coordination Act by Federal agencies, and dumping of wastes in coastal waters under permits of the U.S. Army Corps of Engineers.

Mr. Kitzmiller is a graduate of Yale University and an alumnus of that college's Graduate School of History. He has also been a sailor, newspaper reporter, teacher, and public relations executive.

He has written many articles on environmental subjects and is presently working on a book on environmental problems which is scheduled for publication by American Heritage in the Fall of 1971.

CHAPTER 9

Corporations, Government
and the Environment:

Policy Approaches to a Better
Urban America

Neil H. Jacoby

> *Environmental preservation calls for a redirection of
> our technological efforts, as well as a restructuring of
> patterns of consumption.*

Who would have predicted, even as recently as a year ago, the strong
ground swell of public concern about the environment that now preoccu-
pies Americans? The "great silent majority" as well as activists of the
Left have discovered that our country is running out of clean air and
pure water. Suddenly, we all understand that smog, noise, congestion,
highway carnage, oil-stained beaches, junk graveyards, ugliness and
blatant commercial advertising not only offend our senses but threaten
our health and our very lives.

Having belatedly come to a realization of environmental degradation,
we are trying to identify the culpable parties and to demand corrective
action. It is timely, therefore, to formulate answers to some central
questions. What are the basic forces behind environmental deterioration
and why has a crisis emerged so swiftly? What are the merits of the
several diagnoses and prescriptions that have been advanced for the
environmental problem? How can the environment be improved, and
who should pay the costs? What are the respective roles and responsibilities of business and of government in restoring environmental amenities?
Above all, what lessons does the environmental crisis teach about the
functioning of our political and market systems, and about reforms
needed to forestall other crises in the future?

Focus on the Urban Physical Environment

We focus attention upon the urban physical environment, that is,
upon the spatial and sensory qualities of the land, air, water and phys-

ical facilities that surround the three out of four Americans who live in towns and cities. This *milieu* deteriorates as a result of air and water pollution, noise, industrial and household waste materials, declining quantity or quality of housing *per capita*, crowding, congestion, loss of privacy and recreational facilities, rising accidents and loss of time in urban transportation and—not least—drabness and ugliness.

The physical environment is, of course, only one dimension of man's well-being, of the quality of human life. In focusing upon physical factors, one excludes important social and psychological factors such as order and security, social mobility and social participation or alienation of the individual. All of these environmental factors, along with *per capita* income, wealth, health and education, need enhancement.*

Spatially, the urban environment must be viewed as one subdivision of the entire global ecosystem, which also embraces rural lands, the oceans, the atmosphere surrounding the earth and outer space. Since all parts of this system interact, ideally it should be analyzed, planned and managed as a whole.

The urban physical environment nevertheless merits a top priority because it affects the majority of our population and, by general assent, its qualities are below the threshold of tolerability. In addition, physical factors powerfully influence the health, mental attitudes and life-styles of urban residents, and their enhancement will elevate the social and psychological qualities of American society. One is therefore justified in focusing attention upon the physical characteristics of urban life, notwithstanding that it is but a partial analysis of the global ecosystem.

Causes of Environmental Degradation

Three basic forces have operated to change the urban physical environment for the worse: population concentration, rising affluence and technological change. The overwhelming tendency of people to concentrate in cities has worsened the environment in many ways. Traffic congestion, crowding, overloading of transportation, marketing and living facilities, delays and loss of time, along with rising levels of air, water and noise pollution, have been among the social costs of urbanization. During the half century between 1910 and 1960 the percentage of Americans living in urban areas of 2,500 or more rose from 45.7 to 70, while the number of urbanites tripled from 42 million to 125 million. Beyond doubt, the 1970 Census will reveal an accelerated urbanization.

---

*See the listing of factors in, "Quality of American Life," in *Toward a Social Report* (Washington, D.C.: U.S. Dept. of Health, Education and Welfare, January 1968); also Perloff's tabulation of factors in the urban environment in, Harvey Perloff (Ed.), *The Quality of the Urban Environment* (Baltimore: Johns Hopkins University Press, 1969), pp. 26-29.

Urbanization clearly brings important benefits to people—wider job opportunities, richer educational and cultural fare, more individual freedom from social constraints—or else it would not have been so powerful and enduring a movement. Yet, beyond some levels of population size and density, the total costs of urbanization begin to exceed the total benefits. Discovery of the optimum size of cities and the optimum density of their populations is a vitally important task confronting national planners.

A second prime mover in environmental change has been rising affluence—the expansion of annual real income and expenditure *per capita*. Real income per person (measured in 1958 dollars) more than doubled during the 18 years, 1950-1968, from $1,501 to $3,409. As real incomes have mounted, each person has traveled more miles per year, multiplied his contacts with other people and rapidly expanded his usage of energy. All of this augmented air, water and noise pollution, crowding and congestion and traffic accidents. With the number of urbanites doubling and *per capita* real incomes quadrupling every 40 years, the problem of supplying urban amenities is exploding. One shudders to contemplate the environmental degradation that would occur if 525 million Indians, now crowded 417 per square mile, were each to spend as much as 200 million Americans living only 60 per square mile! India seeks affluence, but could she stand it?

Environmental degradation is not, of course *inherent* in rising affluence. Only the particular forms and methods of production and consumption to which our society has become accustomed degrade it. Rising affluence can and should be a source of environmental enhancement.

It is often overlooked that rising *per capita* income results in an increased demand for environmental amenities. People naturally demand better public goods—more comfort and convenience and beauty in their communities—to match the better private goods and services their rising real incomes enable them to buy. One reason for the environmental "crisis" is the frustration felt by the public with a short supply of environmental amenities available to meet a rising demand for them.

The physical environment of large American cities has not degenerated *absolutely in an overall sense*, but probably has been improving. People easily forget the amenities taken for granted today that were lacking half a century ago. Examples are air-conditioned offices, restaurants and homes; thermostatically controlled electric and gas heat; underground utility wires and poles; paved boulevards and auto freeways. These have widely replaced the crowded slums, the filth of unpaved streets, the drafty cold water flats and belching chimneys of winter and the steaming miseries of unrefrigerated summers. Even in the inner city, people today live longer, healthier and more comfortable lives—if not happier ones—than they did before World War I. What has happened is that (1) the overall supply of urban amenities has fallen far short of the rising effective demand for them, and (2) the supply of certain critical goods, such as pure air and water, has virtually vanished.

The third source of the environmental problem is technological change. Advancing technology has expanded the variety of products available for consumption, made products more complex, raised rates of obsolescence and thereby added to waste disposal. It has also added immensely to the *per capita* consumption of physical materials and energy, with consequent increments of waste and of air and water pollution. It has expanded the amount of information required by consumers to make rational choices in markets, thereby creating market imperfections that are the source of the contemporary "consumerism" movement. Technological change is, however, like rising affluence, a two-edged sword which can be used to improve as well as to degrade the environment. Technology can *reduce* material consumption and recycle harmful wastes. Examples are the replacement of bulky vacuum tubes by micro-miniaturized circuits in computers, or the conversion of sewage into pure water plus fertilizers. Environmental preservation calls for a redirection of our technological efforts, as well as a restructuring of patterns of consumption.

Aspects of Environmental Deterioration

One conspicuous aspect of environmental deterioration has been the disappearance of "free goods"—amenities such as clean air, pure water and open space—that appeared to be in such ample supply relative to the demand for them that their usage was not economized. Pure air is no longer free. To obtain it one must buy air-conditioning equipment and acquire a home in which to install it. Pure water must be purchased by the bottle, now that the product of many municipal water systems is hardly potable. Most urban dwellers must now spend large sums of money in travel in order to gain the privacy and recreation of a natural environment unavailable at home.

A second aspect of environmental change is the fast-rising importance of *spatial relationships* in the cities. Such factors as building heights and population densities, street layout, park location and zoning patterns largely determine the life-styles of urban residents and the supply of amenities available to them. The atrociously bad planning of most American cities and the abject perversion of good zoning and building requirements to serve short-term commercial interests are well-documented facts. The flagrantly overdense building on Manhattan Island has been permitted to occur only because of popular ignorance and apathy. Now, the public is belatedly recognizing the heavy social costs that its neglect has created. Popular concern with city planning, zoning and building development is rising. The heavy stake of the individual in the physical attributes of his community is finally appreciated.

A third aspect of environmental change is the multiplication of *inter-dependencies* among individuals. To an increasing extent the activities of each of us impinge upon others, and affect the utility they derive from their activities. This is so not only because more people live in cities, but also because the scale and variety of each person's activities rise with the amount of real income he produces and consumes. Thus, no one suffered disamenity a generation ago when his neighbor played a phonograph in his suburban home; but many suffer when that neighbor's son now turns up the sound volume of his hi-fi instrument in a high-rise apartment building!

Increasing interdependency is one way of looking at what economists call the "spillover effects" or external costs of production or consumption. For example, paper mills emit chemical wastes into lakes and streams, copper smelters inject sulphur dioxide into the air and electric generating stations throw off carbon monoxide, radioactive wastes or hot water, depending upon their fuels. Motor vehicles cause massive air and noise pollution, traffic accidents, and vast expenditures on medical, legal, policing and engineering services and facilities—all borne mainly by the public. These industries all generate external costs, thrust upon society in the form of loss of environmental amenities. Although reliable estimates are lacking, total external costs in the U.S. economy are of the order of tens of billions of dollars a year.

Swift Rise of the Environmental Problem

The speed with which public interest in the environment has mounted may be explained primarily by the swift decline in certain amenities below thresholds of tolerability. Although certain critical amenities, notably pure air, have been diminishing for many years, the public has suddenly become aware of critical deficiencies. Thus, the quality of air in the Los Angeles basin deteriorated steadily after 1940. Yet only by the mid-1960s, after school children were being advised not to exercise outdoors on smoggy days and when smog alerts were being sounded on many days each year, was decisive action taken to reduce air pollution from motor vehicles. By the sixties, people saw that the "capacity" of the atmosphere over the basin to disperse pollutants had been overloaded beyond the point of toleration.

After the design capacity of any facility has been reached, amenities *per capita* diminish exponentially with arithmetical increases in the load. For example, when a twenty-first person enters an elevator designed to hold twenty persons, everybody in the elevator suffers loss of comfort; and when a twenty-second person enters, the percentage loss of amenity is much greater than the 4.8% increase in the number of passengers. Similarly, when the 5,001st automobile enters a freeway designed to carry 5,000 vehicles per hour, it puts pressure of inadequate space upon 5,001 drivers, and not only upon the new entrant. This appears to explain the rapid recent rise in public awareness of rising external costs.

Another reason for current public concern with the environment is the gathering appreciation of inequity as some groups in society gain benefits at the cost of other groups. The automobilist whose vehicle spews out air pollution gets the benefits of rapid and convenient travel; but he imposes part of the costs of that travel upon people who are forced to breathe bad air and hear deafening noise to the detriment of their health, and who must bear the costs of painting and maintaining property corroded by pollutants. Because this is manifestly inequitable, upgrading the environment by eliminating this kind of pollution will not only add to aggregate real income, but will also improve its distribution.

Illusory Approaches to Environmental Improvement

Before examining effective measures for enhancing the environment let us dispose of a number of partial or superficial diagnoses of, and prescriptions for, this social problem. Several schools of thought have arisen, some of which stand at opposite poles.

First is the Doomsday School, which holds in effect that the problem of environmental degradation is insoluble. Illustrative of the thinking of this school is the book, *The Population Bomb*,* which argues that it is already too late to arrest man's inexorable march to racial extinction through overpopulation, malnutrition, famine and disease. Other cryers of doom are the natural scientists who predict changes in the earth's temperature, as a result of accumulating carbon dioxide in the atmosphere, with consequent melting of the polar ice and other disasters. Although laymen are incompetent to judge these matters, they remain moot issues among natural scientists and therefore at least call for suspended judgment. Accumulating evidence suggests that population growth in the advanced nations has already slowed appreciably, and is starting to do so in many less developed lands. In any event, an apocalyptic view of the future should be rejected if only because it leads to despair and inaction. If one really believes that the future is hopeless, he will cease making an effort to improve society.

At the opposite pole from the Doomsday School is the Minimalist School. It holds that environmental deterioration is a minor problem in comparison with such contemporary issues as poverty, civil rights or educational integration. Its members argue that political leaders calling for a better environment are "eco-escapists," seeking to divert public attention from their failure to resolve these primary issues. What the Minimalists overlook is that the United States is already making prog-

*Ehrlich, Paul R., *The Population Bomb*. New York: Ballantine Books, Inc., 1968.

ress in reducing poverty, expanding civil rights and achieving educational integration, while it is still losing ground in arresting the decline of the urban environment. They also forget that attention to the environment does not mean neglect of poverty. On the contrary, central city areas generally have the worst physical conditions of life and are populated mainly by low-income families. Because the poor stand to gain most from environmental enhancement, a war on pollution is one battlefront in a war on poverty. A vigorous attack on that front need not inhibit action on other fronts.

There is also the Socialist School, whose members view environmental deterioration as an inescapable consequence of capitalist "exploitation." If only private enterprise, market competition and profit incentives were replaced by central planning and state ownership and management of enterprises, they contend, the problem would disappear. However, it is an established fact that the Socialist countries are facing more serious problems of pollution as their *per capita* GNPs are rising. Managers of socialist enterprises are judged by the central planners on the efficiency of their operations, and are under as much pressure to minimize internal costs and to throw as much external cost as possible on the public as are the managers of private firms in market economies who seek to maximize stockholders' profits. Moreover, because a monolithic socialist society lacks a separate and independent mechanism of political control of economic processes, it is less likely to internalize the full costs of production than is a market economy, with its duel systems of market-price and governmental controls. As is noted subsequently, pollution has arison primarily from the failure of our political system, acting through government, to establish desired standards of production and consumption. If government performs its unique tasks, the competitive market system will operate within that framework to produce what the public demands without harming the environment.

The largest group of new environmentalists appear to associate with the Zero Growth School. Its thesis is simple: since environmental degradation is caused by more people consuming more goods, the answer is to stop the growth of population and production. Nature has fixed the dimensions of the natural environment; therefore man should fix his numbers and their economic activities. We must establish a stable relationship between human society and the natural world.

Zero economic and population growth could arrest the process of environmental degradation, but could not, *per se*, restore a good physical environment. Were real GNP constant through time, current levels of air and water pollution, noise, crowding, ugliness and other negative elements would continue, so long as present patterns of production and consumption are maintained.

Zero growth of population and production is, moreover, impossible to achieve. Because economic growth is a product of expanding population, higher investment, and advancing technology, zero growth would call for stopping changes in all three variables. This cannot be done in the proximate future, if at all. A leading population analyst has shown that even if, beginning in 1975, every family in the United States were limited to two children—a heroic assumption—population dynamics are such that this nation would not stop adding people until about 2050 A.D., when it would contain nearly 300 millions.* While a decline in net savings and investment to zero is possible, it is extremely unlikely in view of the savings and investment rates Americans have maintained during the present century in the face of enormous increases in their real wealth and incomes.** A static technology of production is utterly inconceivable. So long as Americans are thinking animals they will increase the productivity of work.

Finally, zero growth is undesirable. A rising GNP will enable the nation more easily to bear the costs of eliminating pollution. Because zero growth of population is far in the distance, and zero growth of output is both undesirable and unattainable, it follows that the environmental problem must be solved, as President Nixon stated in his January, 1970 State of the Union Message, by *redirecting* the growth that will inevitably take place.

The Austerity School of environmental thought is related to the Zero Growth School, because its members assert that environmental decline is produced by excessive use of resources. They are outraged by the fact that the United States consumes about 40% of the world's energy and materials, although it contains only 6% of the world's population. Believing that asceticism is the remedy, they call for less consumption in order to conserve resources and to reduce production and pollution. We should convert ourselves from a society of "wastemakers" into one of "string-savers."

The basic error of the Austerity School is, of course, that it is not the *amount* of production and consumption *per capita* that degrades the environment, but the fact that government has failed to control the *processes* of production and consumption so as to eliminate the pollution associated with them. Without such political action, consumption could be cut in half and society would still suffer half as much pollution; with appropriate political control consumption could be doubled while pollution is radically reduced. The second error of the Austerity School, which distinguishes it from the Zero Growth School, is a notion that the

---

*See Stephen Enke, "Zero Population Growth—When, How, and Why," TEMPO Publication 70TMP35, Santa Barbara, California, June 2, 1970.

**See Policies for Economic Growth and Progress in the Seventies, Report of the President's Task Force on Economic Growth, (Washington, D.C.: U.S. Government Printing Office, 1970).

world confronts a severe shortage of basic natural resources. Exhaustive studies by *Resources for the Future* have revealed, to the contrary, that there are no foreseeable limitations upon supplies of basic natural resources, including energy, at around current levels of cost. Technological progress is continually opening up new supplies of materials that are substitutable for conventional materials (for example, synthetic rubber and fibers) and lowering the costs of alternative sources of energy (for example, production of petroleum products from oil shales, tar sands and coal). Austerity theorists do make a valid point, however, when they observe that governmental regulation to internalize external costs can cause business enterprises to develop ways of recycling former waste materials back into useful channels.

Finally, there is the Public Priorities School of environmental thought. Its adherents see the problem as one of too much governmental spending on defense and space exploration, leaving too little for environmental protection. The solution, as they see it, is to reallocate public expenditures. There are two responses to this line of reasoning: public expenditures are *already* being strongly reordered, and in any event reallocations of *private* expenditures will weigh far more heavily in a solution of the environmental problem. Thus between the fiscal years 1969 and 1971 Federal budget outlays on defense and space are scheduled to shrink by 10%, from $85.5 billion to $77 billion, whereas outlays on social security and public assistance will rise by 26%, from $46 billion to $60 billion.* The President has announced plans for further contractions of defense outlays and expansions of expenditures on the nation's human resources.

Environmental restoration assuredly does require large increases in *public* expenditures upon sewage and water purification, parks, housing, urban development and public transportation. Even more, however, it calls for a reallocation of *private* expenditures as a result of governmental actions to internalize external costs in the private sector. For example, the purchase price and operating expenses of an automobile that is pollution-free will undoubtedly be higher than for a vehicle that degrades the environment, because the auto user will be paying the full costs of his private transportation. With internalization of costs, spending on private auto transportation may be expected to decline *relatively*. At the same time, spending on education and housing, which produce external benefits, will increase relatively. In the aggregate, readjustments in patterns of *private* expenditure will far outweigh reallocation of *public* expenditure in a total program of environmental restoration.

---

*See *Budget of the United States Government, Fiscal Year 1971*, (Washington, D.C.: U.S. Govt. Printing Office, 1971), p. 17.

Environmental Economics and Politics

Because the environmental problem is critically important and is soluble, and neither socialization of the economy, zero growth, austerity nor new public spending priorities offers a satisfactory solution, a more basic approach must be made. A good policy for environmental improvement should improve the distribution of income among people as well as the allocation of society's resources. Governmental intervention is necessary to attain both ends.

Environmental degradation occurs, as has been shown, when there are significant external costs involved in producing or consuming commodities. A social optimum cannot be achieved when there is a divergence between private (internal) and social (external plus internal) costs. An optimal allocation of society's resources requires that the full costs of production of each good or service be taken into account. The internalization of external costs must therefore be a pivotal aim of environmental policy.*

Theoretically, perfectly competitive markets in which there are *no* transaction costs will lead to an optimum reallocation of resources in cases of pollution *via* bargaining between the polluter and the person harmed by pollution, irrespective of which party is legally responsible to compensate the other.** In practice, however, the transaction costs of education, organization and litigation are excessively high when pollution affects large numbers of people, as it usually does. For this reason it is much more efficient for government to resolve pollution problems by legislation or regulation, rather than to leave them to bilateral market bargaining. For example, government can order air polluters to reduce their emissions by X percent. Polluters then incur (internalize) costs in order to conform to the public regulation, thereby relieving the public of even greater costs of maintaining health and property damaged by pollution.

Prior governmental action is essential because the competitive market system is incapable, by itself, of internalizing the costs of antipollution measures. Suppose, for example, that the automobile could be made pollution-free by installing a device costing $X. An automobile owner would not voluntarily install the device, because other people would reap the benefits of the cleaner air made possible by his expenditure. General Motors proved this in 1970 by a well-advertised effort to sell motorists in the Phoenix area a pollution-reducing kit costing only $26. During the first month only a few hundred kits were sold in a market with several

*A trenchant description of the external costs of economic growth is given by E.J Mishan, *The Costs of Economic Growth*, (New York: Praeger, 1967).

**See R.H. Coase, "The Problem of Social Costs," *Journal of Law and Economics*, III (October 1960).

hundred thousand potential buyers! Nor would auto makers voluntarily install the device, because this would add to their costs and put them at a disadvantage in competition with other manufacturers who did not install it. And antitrust laws prohibit any *agreement* among all auto manufacturers simultaneously to install, or not to install, pollution-reducing devices. Where large external costs or benefits are involved, there is a conflict between the decision that serves the self-interest of the individual and that which serves the collective welfare of the community. Community welfare can only be given the precedence it deserves by a prior governmental action regulating private behavior, followed by corporation actions to modify products, prices and allocations of resources so as to conform to the public regulation.

Society cannot reasonably expect individual enterprises or consumers to shoulder external costs in the name of "social responsibility," because the competitive market system puts each firm and household under strong pressure to minimize its costs in order to survive. What is needed is a prior political decision that leaves all producers or consumers in the same relative position.

There are usually alternative solutions to pollution problems, and one task is to evaluate each alternative in order to identify the least-cost solution. Consider again the example of smog in the Los Angeles basin. Among possible ways of coping with this problem are the following: controlling emissions of pollutants from motor vehicles and stationary sources by public regulation; moving people out of the basin; rezoning to reduce building density; building a rapid mass transit system; imposing heavy taxes on private automobile operation; or subsidizing motorists to limit their auto mileage. The costs and benefits of each alternative, and combinations thereof, should be evaluated before an anti-pollution policy is adopted. The goal should always be the most efficient use of scarce resources.

All desirable things in limited supply have a cost, and there are trade-offs between desirable things. People may gain more of one thing only by sacrificing something else, and the optimum situation is reached when no additional benefits can be obtained by further substitutions. These principles apply to environmental amenities. For example, noise pollution can be reduced with benefits to health and well-being, but at the cost of larger expenditures for insulation or noise-abatement devices or a reduction in the speed or power of engines. Conceivably, utter silence could be achieved by incurring astronomical costs and by making great sacrifices of mobility, power and time. The public decides the *optimum* noise level by balancing the benefits of less noise against the costs of attaining it. Government then fixes a noise standard at that point where the costs of reducing noise further would exceed the additional benefits to health and well-being. Although the calculus is necessarily rough, this is the rationale of determining standards to reduce pollution of all kinds. We assume that somehow people's utility functions are combined into social preference functions that determine the optimum levels of quality of the various environmental factors. This combinatorial process is carried out by the political system of our society, about which more is said later on.

Assessing the Costs of Environmental Improvement

Just as governmental intervention is needed to bring about the reallocations of resources needed for environmental improvement, so it is also required to levy the costs of such improvement equitably among individuals and groups in society so as to improve—or at least prevent a worsening of—the distribution of income.

There are opposite approaches to the problem of cost allocation. By one principle, polluters should pay the costs of suppressing their pollution; by another, the public should pay polluters to stop polluting. The second principle is defended on the ground that the public benefits from the reduction of pollution and should pay the costs of this benefit. Those who espouse this view hold that tax credits and public subsidies are the proper instruments of a policy for environmental betterment. Libertarians usually favor this approach because of their preference for the "carrot" versus the "stick," and their belief that public boards often come under the domination of those they are supposed to regulate.

Advocates of the first principle argue, to the contrary, that society initiates an anti-pollution policy from a current status of inequity. The problem is to *restore equity* as between polluters and those damaged by pollution, not to compensate polluters for a loss of equitable rights. They also observe that persons with large incomes generally generate disproportionately more pollution than those with low incomes, so that a policy of internalizing costs in the polluter will tend to shift income from richer to poorer people, with resulting gains in social well-being. The appropriate instruments for dealing with pollution are, in their view, public regulations to reduce harmful activities, or taxes and fines on polluters.

Equity requires that the costs of suppressing environmental damage be borne by those responsible for it. Public restraint of private actions harmful to the environment thus should be the dominant instrument of environmental policy. Assertion of this principle does not, however, preclude the use of taxes, fines or lawsuits, nor does it rule out the use of public subsidies to enterprises which, through long continued tolerance of harmful activities vital to their survival, have acquired a certain equity in them. For example, a city council might prohibit billboard advertising of off-premise goods or services, on the ground that the visual pollution costs borne by the public exceed the benefits. To enable outdoor advertising companies to finance an adjustment into other activities, a city might reasonably offer to pay them subsidies over a period of years on a descending scale.

Environmental Policy Instruments

Since the quality of the urban environment is a function of many variables, public policies to enhance the environment must utilize many instruments.

One key instrument, as noted previously, is direct governmental control of emissions of pollutants—audial, atmospheric, olfactory, visual or health-affecting. This approach is now exemplified in Federal and state laws governing air and water pollution, and in Federal standards of noise emissions from aircraft engines. Assuming that reduction of emissions is the least-cost solution, the main problems are to determine appropriate standards and to enforce them. In fixing standards, the state of pollution control technology is an important consideration. Where such technology exists and can be applied at reasonable cost, the law should simply *ban* emissions and enforce compliance. This appears to be true of much air and water pollution from fixed sources, such as the chimneys of manufacturing and power-generating plants. Where pollution technology is in process of development, as in the case of automobile emissions, government should fix standards that are *progressively raised* through time.

Another way to internalize external costs is to guarantee each property owner legal rights to the amenities pertaining to his property. A California court recently awarded substantial damages to homeowners near the Los Angeles International Airport to compensate them for demonstrated loss of property values because of excessive noise from overflying airplanes. A constitutional amendment should be enacted guaranteeing every property owner a right to environmental amenities, because this would induce business enterprises to reduce or eliminate pollution in order to escape legal liabilities. However, judicial processes are so costly, time-consuming and uneven in their results as to make other solutions to environmental problems preferable.

Governments—Federal, state and local—are themselves copious contributors to air and water pollution, especially by discharging untreated sewage into rivers and lakes. They should internalize these costs by massive public expenditures on sewage treatment and water purification plants. Such outlays will, of course, ultimately be paid for by a public that presumably values the benefits of a clean environment more highly than the money paid in taxes to finance such facilities.

Urban planning, zoning and building regulations are powerful instruments for enhancing the amenities of space, privacy, recreation, housing, transportation and beauty in our cities. If American cities are to offer ample amenities for living, *much stronger governmental controls* of the design, quality, height and density of buildings, and of the layout of transportation, recreation and cultural facilities will be necessary. Americans will have to put a much higher priority on urban amenities, if strong enough instruments of social control over property usage are to be forged. Such controls will be opposed by builders, accustomed as they are to permissive public regulation that can be bent to their purposes. Yet firm public control of land usage under a long-range metropolitan plan is one reason why such cities as London hold a strong attraction for their residents as well as for millions of foreign visitors.*

Enlargement of the supply of urban amenities also calls for immense public and private expenditures on recreational and cultural facilities, housing and public transportation systems. The many programs coming under the aegis of the auspices of the Federal Departments of Transportation and of Housing and Urban Development are instruments to this end. A whole battery of incentives for the participation of private enterprise in the gargantuan tasks will need to be fabricated, including tax credits, accelerated depreciation, credit guarantees, cost-plus contracts and direct governmental subsidies. The naive idea that private corporations can or will undertake urban rehabilitation out of a sense of "social responsibility" denies the ineluctable fact that in a competitive market economy the firm cannot devote a material part of its resources to unprofitable activities and survive. Just as government must first create a market for pollution-reducing devices before the enterprise system will produce them, so it must first create adequate incentives to induce enterprises to produce urban housing and transit systems. That the responses are swift when the incentives are strong is shown by the great strength of the housing boom after World War II, triggered by liberal FHA mortgage insurance and Veterans Administration home loan guarantees.

Above all, a high-quality urban environment requires the public to assign high values to urban amenities—to appreciate them greatly and to work hard and pay much for them. So far, too few American urbanites have held such values with sufficient intensity to bring about the necessary political action. Whether recent public outcries for a better environment will be sufficiently strong, sustained and widespread to change the historical American posture of indifference remains to be seen.

Improving the Political and Market Systems

The sudden emergence of the environmental problem raises profound issues about the functioning of our social institutions. Does it betoken an institutional breakdown—a failure to respond to new demands of the public? Has the social system responded, but been seriously laggard in its responses? Does the fault lie mainly in the political or in the market

*See "If Only Other Cities Were Like London," *Business Week,* May 30, 1970.

subsystem of our society, wherein there are two methods by which social choices of the uses of resources are made—voting in elections and buying in markets?

Although these questions cannot be answered finally, the most defensible positions appear to be these: first, the social system has been sluggish in responding to the higher values placed by the public on environmental amenities, but it has not broken down and the processes of resource reallocation have begun. Second, the environmental crisis was generated primarily by tardy responses of the political system, and only secondarily by faults in the market system.

If American society is to attain optimal well-being, its dual set of political and market controls must operate promptly and in the proper sequence in response to changes in social values. Political action is first needed to create a demand for environment-improving products; market competition can then assure that this demand is satisfied economically. Measures are needed to improve both political and market processes.

Our model of the dynamic relationships between changes in social values, government actions and corporate behavior is depicted in Figure 1. The *primary* sequential flow of influence runs from changes in social values, *via* the political process, to changes in governmental regulation of the private sector and reallocation of public resources; thence, *via* the market process, to corporate reallocation of private resources. However, changes in social values are not wholly determined by shifts in levels of income and other autonomous factors. They also respond to political leadership in the legislative and executive branches of government and to the public advertising and selling efforts of corporations. Similarly, governmental actions are not responsive exclusively to shifts in the values of the public. They are also influenced in some degree by the political activities of businessmen and by corporate lobbying. These secondary flows of influence also help to determine the performance of the social system.

The model enables us to identify salient points of improvement in the system. They are (1) to reform the political process so that governmental actions will more rapidly and accurately reflect significant shifts in social values, (2) to reform the market process so that corporate behavior will more rapidly and accurately reflect changes in governmental regulation, and (3) to reform political and business behavior so that their secondary influences will be facilitative rather than obstructive. Specifically, what changes are needed in each of these three areas?

The environmental problem emphasizes once again the need for a political system capable of translating changes in social values rapidly and accurately into governmental actions. The political apparatus for sensing, recording, mobilizing, transmitting and acting upon millions of changes in individual preferences must be improved. Our representative system of government must be made more representative. This raises

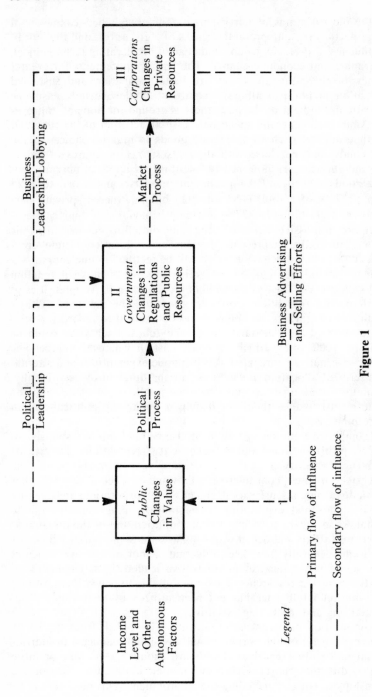

Figure 1

Dynamic Relationships Between Public Values, Governmental Regulations and Corporate Resource Allocations

anew the old dilemmas of participative democracy, the weaknesses of political parties, the unrepresentativeness of legislatures, and the inordinate influence of pressure groups in an age of accelerating technological, demographic and economic change. The basic requirements for greater efficiency of the political system are better education and sustained participation in political affairs by citizens. While one may easily be pessimistic in the light of the past, there is ground for hope of improvement. Americans generally spend only a small fraction of the time and effort they devote to choosing private goods in making choices of the public goods they purchase with their taxes. Yet purchases of public goods and services are now nearly one-third as large as purchases of private goods. During 1969 government purchases amounted to $225 billion or 23% of a total GNP of $923 billion, whereas private purchases were $698 billion or 77%. Rational behavior in resource allocation requires a massive increase in the time and effort devoted to public decisions. Hopefully, the present egregious underallocation of time represents a cultural lag in behavior which will be rectified in due course.

Changes should be made in the voting process to make it function more like a market. Just as consumers record the relative intensities of their demands for different private goods by the amounts of their expenditures in markets, so voters could be enabled to record the relative intensities of their demands for public goods. Each voter could be given, say, 1000 votes, which he could cast in whatever numbers he chose for alternative aggregate levels of public expenditures and alternative patterns of allocation of each level among different objects. Finally, a maximum usage of direct links between public expenditures and the taxes levied to finance them could help to make the political system more responsive.

The competitive market system must also be made more responsive to shifts in public values and governmental regulations. Despite its undoubted superiority as a device for gauging consumers' wants, the recent rise of the "consumerism" movement reflects, among other things, a disturbing insensitivity of the business corporations to changing public demands and expectations. The foot-dragging behavior of the auto makers in regard to safety and air pollution and of the oil companies in regard to air and ocean-water pollution is symptomatic. Business corporations generally have been reluctant, if not obstructive, reactors to new social values instead of innovative leaders in satisfying them. Either their market researchers have been unable to detect them, or else correct market intelligence has not been utilized by their engineering, manufacturing and marketing executives.

A reorientation of corporate organization is needed, from the board of directors down through corporate and divisional managers to individual plant and store executives. The board should include one or more "outside" directors chosen especially for their knowledge of corporate relationships to society, including the environment. This need should be met by the normal process of including such nominees in the slate of directors presented by management for stockholder vote, rather than by augmenting the board by *special* stockholder nominees, as Ralph Nader proposed to General Motors Corporation. The normal procedure is much more likely to result in effective board action to improve the environment, because it avoids "bloc" politics within the board. Every single policy and action of the firm should be reviewed for its effect upon the environment. An Environmental Analyst, assigned to this task as a staff adviser to the Chief Executive, would help to assure good corporate behavior. Standard corporate policy should require all managers to include in their proposals for new operations of facilities measures for preventing adverse environmental effects. Corporations should also make more penetrating use of consumer surveys and public opinion polls *in order* to keep informed of shifts in public tastes and priorities.

Reforms are also needed to ensure that the secondary influences upon social values exercised by political and business leaders are facilitative rather than obstructive. These influences are significant. For example, President Eisenhower's sponsorship of the Interestate Highway Act in 1956 and President Kennedy's proposal of a manned round trip to the moon in 1961 mobilized and activated changes in the values of the American people which led to highway and space programs each of the order of $5 billion a year. President Nixon's leadership in 1970 in a national effort to improve the environment will probably produce even larger reallocations of resources. All three presidents discerned deep changes in public priorities to which they gave form and implementation. Without such political leadership, readjustments would have been delayed amid mounting public tension and frustration.

American corporate leadership generally has *not* played a facilitative role in implementing changes in social values. Whereas business lobbyists should be informing legislators of new environmental regulations desired by the public, they usually oppose such changes. Most corporate advertising is narrowly focused upon expanding public demand for existing products rather than for new products with superior environmental effects. As Henry Ford recently advised, corporate managers should "stop thinking about changing public expectations as new costs which may have to be accepted but certainly have to be minimized. Instead, we should start thinking about changes in public values as opportunities to profit by serving new needs."*

New Perspectives on Social Progress

This analysis of deterioration in the urban environment and of means to restore it has unveiled neither a master culprit nor a panacea. It has delineated a complex public problem requiring many instruments of

---

*Address to the Public Affairs Forum of the Harvard Business School. See *Wall Street Journal*, February 17, 1970.

policy for its solution. It has shown that the *basic* requirement is a citizenry that assigns higher values to urban amenities than it has in the past, and will work harder and pay more to get them. Given new social preferences, new regulations will be imposed and those long neglected regulations on the statute books will finally be enforced. It is disturbing to reflect that a lawsuit brought by the Attorney General of the United States early in 1970 against several large corporations for polluting the southern end of Lake Michigan was to enforce a Federal statute enacted in 1899! Here—as in the administration of urban zoning codes—Americans have not put high enough values upon environmental amenities to insist that private actions conform to existing public laws.

Environmental improvement will call for annual public and private expenditures of tens of billions of dollars indefinitely into the future. Profound changes will be necessary in the structure of relative costs and prices of goods, and in patterns of production and consumption. These readjustments will cause difficulties for individual companies operating on the margin of profitability and unable to pay the full costs of their products. Yet the ability of our profit-oriented enterprise system to adapt to a massive internalization of costs cannot be doubted, when one recalls its successful assimilation of the technological revolution since World War II. Over a period of time the costs and prices of products with large external costs (for example, automobiles) would rise relatively, while those with large external benefits (for example, homes) would decline relatively. While consumers would spend relatively less on autos and relatively more on housing, in a growing economy this would mean changes in the growth rates of different industries rather than an absolute decline in the output of any one. Also, new industries would emerge to supply the growing demand for pollution-controlling equipment and services. Profit rates and market signals would continue to guide resources in the directions desired by consumers.

The effects of environmental improvement upon the overall growth of the U.S. economy depend mainly upon how "economic growth" is defined and measured. There is a growing recognition that the true end of public policy is a steady expansion of social well-being, and that a rising GNP is only a means to this end. Gross national product is simply a measure of the aggregate output of the economy, whereas social well-being is also directly related to the composition of output, its full costs, and the uses to which it is put. If, as has been true during the past 20 years, much production included in the GNP has been associated with national defense and environmental degradation, growth of the GNP can be a highly misleading index of gains in social well-being. Indices of well-being should be developed to help guide long-term public policy, and GNP also should be recast to provide a more meaningful measure of total output.*

*See John W. Kendrick, "Restructuring the National Income Accounts for Investment and Growth Analysis," *Statistik Tidscrift*, 1966. P. 5.

Assuming the existence of a strong effective demand by the public for a better urban environment, it cannot be doubted that a redirection of production to supply that demand will expand the well-being of American society. A better environment would enable people to reduce many other costs they now incur for health, property maintenance, recreation and travel to leave uncongenial surroundings. Rising social well-being is not in conflict with an expanding GNP, provided that the increments of production improve the quality of life. On the contrary, growth of production is needed for that purpose. As President Nixon wrote: "The answer is not to abandon growth, but to redirect it."*

To rehabilitate the environment, to raise the quality of American life, will require billions of dollars, vast ingenuity, and years of time. Above all, it will call for sustained efforts by the public, arising from deeply held values. Our nation has the resources, the technology and the time to complete the task, and can make the necessary institutional changes. The question that remains is whether we, the people, possess the sense of dedication and commitment necessary for an enduring effort.

Neil H. Jacoby is a graduate of the University of Saskatchewan, receiving his B.A. in 1930, and his LL.D. in 1950. He also attended the University of Chicago, where he received his Ph.D. in 1938.

At present he is Chairman of President Nixon's Task Force on U.S. Economic Growth and Professor of Business Economics and Policy at the University of California, Los Angeles. He was formerly Dean of the graduate School of Business Administration at U.C.L.A. Since 1957 he has served as U.S. representative in the Economic and Social Council of the United Nations, and from 1953 to 1955 he was on President Eisenhower's Council of Economic Advisers.

Dr. Jacoby is the author of many books, including *Can Prosperity Be Sustained* (1956), *U.S. Aid to Taiwan* (1966), and *European Economics: East and West* (1967). In addition he is a member of the advisory committee and editorial board of the *Journal of Finance*; a member of the editorial board on *Petroleum Industry Studies*, Yale University Press; and an Associate of the Center for the Study of Democratic Institutions in Santa Barbara.

*State of the Union Message to the Congress, January 22, 1970.

CHAPTER 10

The Environmental Bandwagon

And Some Other Matters Concerning the Future of the Human Race

Alexander King

> *. . . pollution and the other environmental problems are but symptoms and . . . the disease itself is so much more deeply imbedded in our society that attack on the symptoms alone can be but a minor palliative.*

Present concern with the environment is a cautionary example of how man attempts to cure the ills of the human condition. The need for action is, of course, all too clear—noisy and culturally sterile cities cluttered with automobiles and solid waste, filthy air, undrinkable water and polluted beaches are evidence enough to justify public indignation and clamor. Manifestations however have risen to the pitch of hysteria, and a whole army of self-styled ecologists, fanatical conservationists and zero-growthers has arisen in whom ignorance and emotionalism are perfectly matched. At the same time there is a growing suspicion that politicians are gleefully seizing onto the movement as a timely diversion. Is not pollution a common enemy, against which the whole nation, or still better the whole world can unite and which does not, like human enemies, fight back?

Pollution is of course no new phenomenon. It was, if possible, still more ugly during the height of the industrial revolution in Europe. In England, for example, the northern mining villages with their terraced rows of squalid houses are still evidence of this, while the lethal "peasoup" fogs of London so prevalent in Dickens' time were a good deal worse than anything experienced in America today. But these were accepted by a generally docile population as facts of life or acts of God rather than of man. In London, indeed much has been done; the peasoupers are now a matter of history and there have been no killer-fogs for a decade, while better sewage disposal methods have brought oxygen back into the rivers. Fish have returned to the Thames for the first time in 20 years. The transformation of Pittsburgh is another example which makes the older inhabitants wonder what all the present fuss of pollution is about.

The environmental hysteria is, in essential, a symbolic protest of men against the encroaching grip of technology on the quality of individual life, a swing of the pendulum from the euphoric decades when science and technology were matters of national pride and utopian hope.

Expenditure on research and development (R&D) by the industrialized nations of the world has been growing exponentially over the last 200 years and is only now beginning to flatten out. The national goals to which this mounting effort has been aimed have been essentially defense, national prestige and economic growth. As technological knowledge accumulated, however, politicians and the public have increasingly questioned the validity of national research programs, despite the space triumphs, and have begun to fear their accumulating consequences. Vietnam has made this questioning come somewhat earlier; it would have come in any case. The demystification of science is however due less to the bomb and biological warfare than to the creeping incursion of technology on the daily lives of men and women everywhere; in cities the evidence is ever-present, while radio and television bring a sense of the richness, emptiness and squalor of contemporary industrial life even to the remote village recesses of the Third World.

The main theme of this paper is that pollution and the other environmental problems are but symptoms and that the disease itself is so much more deeply imbedded in our society that attack on the symptoms alone can be but a minor palliative.

The Problems of Contemporary Society

Until recently, man has been preoccupied mainly by the struggle upwards from the subsistence level; like the cow, the greater part of our lives has been devoted to maintenance of the body, reproduction and the renewal of sleep, with only statistically small proportions for cerebration and poetry. This struggle for subsistence is still the main objective of the majority of humans, not yet free from hunger, provided with insufficient shelter, insecure from the attack of enemies and only partially masters over nature. The small proportion of humans who have now climbed out of the primeval state and who form the industrialized societies has done so with the aid of technology, often too brutally impoverishing the world's resources and degrading the environment in the process. This is no new characteristic of humanity. The turning into desert of the Middle East and the Gobi region, the soil erosion of Africa and many other examples indicate that man's struggle for economic improvement has often been shortsighted and to the deterioration of his environment. Increased density of population is bringing this trend to the level of global crisis. In addition to degradation of the natural environment, man's artificial and urban environment is becoming intolerable. *Mere* size and urban sprawl are uncomfortable enough and make it difficult for life in city centers and faceless suburbs to be truly human and creative; the cluttering of streets by the automobile, bad air, noise and the sad repetitive movements of the commuter bring frustration to the city dweller and worker, while traffic problems in the air and on the surface as well as the soaring death rate from highway accidents provide little comfort.

Such conditions are building up to social disequilibrium—high rates of crime, delinquency and drug taking, and the alienation of a large number of people who can be supported in some sort of way by the generalized affluence which surrounds them. These people see no point in working hard for a living and reject the contemporary values of the consumer society; they have an increasing resistance to control, discipline and planning by decision makers who appear remote in time and understanding from those lives they control; they have a general sense of individual alienation and isolation.

Then there is the growing complex of educational problems, a realization that young people are being trained for life in a world that is evaporating, rather than for the future in which they will live and work. Innovation in the educational system is imperative, but the resistance is enormous. The university is an acute example, with a large and increasing proportion of the age group retained in a quasi-adolescent ghetto, without responsibility, well into their twenties, in establishments inherently academic and created to provide for the relatively small proportion of those with a devotion to scholarship or a well-defined professional vocation. This situation inevitably leads to frustration and confrontation, whatever the socio-political system, and makes for instability of society, individual alienation and political exploitation.

Finally there are the problems of islands of poverty, underprivilege and intolerance within the affluent society and the great mass of undifferentiated misery and hopelessness in the Third World outside.

These problems seem to arise from the following interrelated causes: (1) population growth and its concentration in cities, (2) high general levels of prosperity—despite residual poverty, and (3) the unwanted side-effects of that same technology on which economic growth and prosperity depend.

The above three factors are, of course, individually matters of concern, and the intensity of their interaction varies from place to place all over the globe. Okita, the Japanese economist, regards population per acre of utilizable land as a useful indicator of the general social problem intensity. Furthermore, attack on each single cause will have repercussions on the others. For example, attack on population problems demands the creation of new scientific ideas and a new technology of contraception which can also have widespread social and psychological effects.

Economic *growth* is still a key question in situations in which economists are still the only scientific mandarins with direct influence on
national policy formation. In May 1970, the Ministers of the Organization for Economic Cooperation and Development (OECD) countries,
which account for about three-quarters of international trade and R&D
output as well as 90% of the financial aid given to the underdeveloped
countries, discussed the growth prospects of the next ten years. The
decade of the 1960s has seen the overattainment of a goal of 50%
increase in the gross national product of the member countries, an
increase which would have approached 60% had Japan (not a member at
the beginning of the decade) been included. For the period up to 1980,
they "set an increase in the real national product of the OECD area as a
whole, of the order of 65% as a collective growth objective" being a
framework within which the national economic policies would be determined. This was, however, followed by an exceedingly important quali-
fication—"Ministers stressed that growth is not an end in itself but rather
an instrument for creating better conditions of life. Increased attention
must be given to the qualitative aspects of growth and to the formula-
tion of policies with respect to the broad economic and *social* choices
involved in the allocation of resources." They then continued by
stressing the importance of the environment.

International Discussion of Environmental Problems

Within the great complex of societal problems then, the pollution
symptoms have been chosen for special attention. The environmental
manifestations of the United States are well known to the readers of this
book. This section will limit itself to describing how the various international organizations are jumping onto the bandwagon.

Some of the UN special agencies for a long time have considered
aspects of pollution of direct relevance within their mandates, especially
in the obvious example of the World Health Organization (WHO) and
the Food and Agriculture Organization (FAO). The Organization for
Economic Cooperation and Development has, over a period of years,
developed a modest but practical program in technological and resource
management aspects of air and water systems as well as studies on
pesticides, urban noise, the supersonic boom, urban management, road
safety research and new technological possibilities in transportation.
This work will now be given greater emphasis and extended within the
economic context which is the characteristic of this organization, with
special stress on cost-benefit and cost-effectiveness studies of alternative
means of controlling pollution, including the probelm of who should
pay—the state, industry or consumer, a matter which involves competitive aspects of international trade.

Next, President Nixon, in addition to initiating action programs and a complex governmental machine for pollution-control within the United States, called upon the Atlantic Council to take up the challenge of the problems of the modern society (a cliché invented by OECD) with the result that NATO has created a committee for the purpose and has stimulated a series of national case studies, mainly, of course, on pollution—of inland and coastal waters, air, *et cetera*. The United States Government has also taken a lead in hoisting other international organizations onto the wagon.

The Council of Europe, which for many years has interested itself in ecological problems, held an important meeting on the environment earlier this year in the presence of many Princes of the European Royal Houses. The Economic Commission for Europe of the United Nations is equally concerned and provides a forum for East-West discussion of these problems; it will hold an important conference in Prague during 1971. The European Communities of Brussels are also considering these questions from a more directly operational point of view within the scope of its "Agrain Committee." The United Nations Educational, Scientific, and Cultural Organization (UNESCO) with its cultural and research preoccupations held a world conference on the biosphere in 1969, while the UN itself is organizing a gigantic world conference on the environment which will be held in Stockholm in 1972, and for which all the specialized agencies are being marshaled and coordinated into providing a composite input.

In most of the European countries, governmental organization for such matters is highly fragmented across the governmental machine and central authority or even coordination is hardly yet established. Those few officials, often representing very thin research activities and functional policies, are threatened with having to spend a large part of their time traveling from one international committee to the next.

Apart from these and other intergovernmental approaches, a large number of learned bodies have begun to take an interest in the problems of modern society and, being free from the sectoral and bureaucratic constraints of the governmental bodies, are able to take a broader and more comprehensive view, but lack, of course, the means of action. They possess a limited degree of influence but have an important function with regard to public education in establishing interdisciplinary communication between specialists. They also provide an opportunity for deeper intellectual penetration than is possible in the councils of governments. I shall list only three examples from the numerous recent meetings on this topic—the symposium of the Nobel Foundation held in October 1969, the New York Conference of the World Academy of Arts and Sciences on "Environment and Society" in April 1970, and the Aspen Conference of the International Association for Cultural

Freedom on "Technology: Social Goals and Cultural Options" of August 1970. All these meetings have had an integrative and comprehensive approach to the problematique and have produced a surprising consensus among natural scientists, economists and the behavioral scientists. On the environment again, the Batelle Institute is organizing an important conference in Washington, D.C., in January 1971, where the responsibilities of industry will be particularly stressed; this will be followed by a similar conference in Europe later that year. Even the International Chamber of Commerce has chosen "The Environment" as the main theme for its 1971 meetings.

So the bandwagon rolls right merrily. Of course much of use will come out of all this activity, and the subject is inherently so important that one must only hope that present enthusiasms will not be followed by a pendulum swinging toward neglect and under-emphasis. This is by no means improbable, especially as of the moment so much of the clamor and fury is merely verbal, and the proportion of R&D effort devoted to pollution problems is—in most countries—trivially small. Furthermore, until recently the scientific problems involved in pollution have not been sufficiently interesting to attract the attention of many first-class scientific brains. Most of the experimental work is conducted in government laboratories, with restricted initiative—and pedestrian thinking.

In fact we face the environmental problem through a miasma of ignorance, and much new and break-through research is required if serious progress is to be made. For example, two separate geo-scientific approaches predict that: (1) there will be a serious heating up of our planet by the end of the century caused by the accumulation of carbon dioxide in the upper atmosphere, which results from excessive combustion and a dwindling proportion of the earth's surface covered with chlorophyl-bearing plants that maintain the oxygen level, and (2) another group of physicists, alarmed by the discovery of liquid water at the base of the Antarctic ice cap, suggest that the ice will, before long, slide into the ocean, devastate the world with monstrous tidal waves and trigger off the next ice age. It may well be that both or neither of these movements are to be taken seriously, but it would be good to know the probabilities. It might be interesting to envisage a U.S.—U.S.S.R. cooperative scheme for the use of atomic power to shave off the surface encrustments of ice in Antarctica—for the survival of the race.

Much of the ignorance and prejudice which bedevils environmental discussions stems from a lack of knowledge of the cross-impacts of particular pollutants on quite different activities, and *vice versa*. For example, it is increasingly clear that eutrophication* of lakes and inland

*The mechanism which produces an irreversible pollution in lakes and inland seas—a notable case being Lake Erie.

seas results from the runoff of soluble fertilizers and the phosphate pollution from detergents, but agricultural policy—especially with its objective of growing more food for expanding populations—seldom takes account of such matters. Then there is the notorious example of DDT, man's man-made enemy *number one*, now banned in many countries. Yet this chemical, which probably cut a year off the Second World War, has probably saved about 200,000 lives for every individual it has even slightly harmed. This is, of course, not necessarily an argument for continuing its use, but if we are serious about the developing countries we should stop and think a little longer. It is easy to argue that the world would be better off without the millions of people now living as a result of DDT, but this is hardly an argument to appeal to the sentimental ecologists. Banning of DDT by all industrialized countries is conceivable and possibly desirable, but it will be difficult to persuade the developing nations to abandon the use of this chemical—so important for their agricultural and hence economic development, as well as the control of malaria and other insect-borne diseases. The continuing use of such chemicals by the under-developed countries will mean a continued accumulation of toxic substances in the ocean. This is but one of the many examples of conflict between economic betterment and environmental control.

There is great need therefore for a better sense of proportion on these matters, and this can only be obtained through more knowledge—and in particular, knowledge of the way to manage large and complex systems. This brings us back to the problematique.

Is a Moratorium Desirable or Possible?

If the web of problems now facing society is caused by combined forces of affluence, high population density and technology it seems reasonable to propose a control of population and urban expansion, putting a stop to economic growth and calling a halt to technology and to the scientific research on which it depends. Hence a new flurry of seminars on zero growth calls for a moratorium on science, *et cetera*. These are clamors which are likely to become louder and which cannot be lightly dismissed. What is true is that the disruption of society and the body politic which would result from such action, as well as the new crop of ensuing problems, would probably produce a chaos greater than we have today.

The noble savage is not such an easy concept when developed in terms of the inhabitants of megalopolis.

First, the slowing down of growth at the present stage with its islands of poverty within the affluent world and the mass of subsistence misery in the greater world outside would hardly be acceptable socially or politically. To the underprivileged in advanced societies it would appear as economic treachery, to the Third World it would seem a final abdication of responsibility on the part of the post-colonialist industrial countries. It should be noted that even now in some European countries obsessed by the "technological gap," the present U.S. policies of stressing the environment are seen as a political diversion from the apparently still necessary effort to increase growth through industrial strength fed by the cornucopia of new technology. Eventually, of course, world needs to conserve natural resources will slow down economic growth—shortage of paper could be one of the earliest symptoms—but this is for the day after tomorrow. What is needed is a new attitude toward growth, a clearer definition of national goals and an effort to use human wisdom and management skills toward their achievement. It is of note that even with the large growth rate expected for the next decade, social demand—especially for education, better cities and transportation—will mop up most of the growth, leaving little extra for the individual pay packet. Indeed it begins to appear that in a successful capitalistic system the stage will be reached at which social costs will begin to dominate over individual profit.

In preparing new growth policies it is now imperative to devise an indicator more suitable than GNP—one which will take into account the quality and welfare aspects. Social accounting has become an essential need, but we appear to be far from achieving it. In general there is a need for a new socio-economic theory. Can our economists provide it?

If growth is to be maintained—as a means rather than an end—technology will still be required to produce it. But this must not be the old polluting exploitative technology with which we are familiar; its control as also the evaluation of its economic, social and cultural effects will have to be guided by the same socio-economic considerations we have mentioned. This in turn will require new attitudes on the part of industry. In fact there are signs that a few of the larger multinational firms are reassessing their functions, beyond the elementary one of profit making; undoubtedly they are responding to the signs of the times. However, long-term self-interest on the part of capitalist industry may well necessitate the adoption of a modicum of social responsibility.

Evaluation of the probable consequences of alternative technological decisions will inevitably become a national and, because it is a very costly business, international affair. There is every reason why technology should be made to serve human ends, but these ends must be made explicit and the boundary conditions established. Much the same can be said concerning science as such; knowledge now, as always, can be good and evil in its application. What is lacking is human wisdom. Inexorably we are brought back to the first chapter of Genesis; good and evil are equally germinal within each new item of uncovered knowledge. Having accepted the burden of knowledge several millennia ago, there is no going back; what is lacking is the wisdom which should be the organic companion of knowledge.

A case of particular promise and danger now being unveiled by science is to be found at the interface of biology, neurology, molecular biology, psychology and genetic engineering. The whole range of new possibilities presented by an understanding of how the cerebral mechanism operates and can be modified could lead to a man-made evolution toward a creature superior to man as we know him. Alternatively, lacking the wisdom of man to play God, this new knowledge could be a means for his destruction more subtle and more monstrous than his other plaything, the bomb. There have been several recent discussions of this subject at the Center for the Study of Democratic Institutions. Together with the possibility of control and modification of the nervous system comes influence over life and death, control (as ever for good *and* evil) of human potentiality and achievement. The new biological knowledge is already beginning to have its influence on social problems. For example, if, as it appears, the irreversible biological process which determines a child's capacity for learning throughout his life is established in the first few months of life, present policies for equality of opportunity, for education, become a marginal and very expensive aberration. The creation of new knowledge has been an intrinsic human characteristic since the Garden of Eden, and any attempt to stop it would be futile. Once again we have to conclude with Harvey Cox that we must not "leave it to the snake" but encourage the pursuit of wisdom rather than the mere unearthing of new information to extend man's already overweaponed physique.

Recently the "Year 2000" group of the European Cultural Foundation, meeting at Bellagio, called for the creation of a European (and eventually World) Council to consider the consequences of the new biology for man and for his planet. Such a Council is, no doubt, necessary but if, as is probable, it would be constituted from clever and powerful rather than wise men, it could all too easily prove to be yet another vested interest group for the manipulation of man. All in all, it might be wise if such a council would give initial and perhaps unique support to genetic engineering applied to that delightful and clever creature the porpoise, as a possible replacement of *homo sapiens*.

The Problematique and the Club of Rome

It has been argued that the present cluster of multi-variant, universal and interacting problems can no longer be attacked, with any hope of success, though the conventional mechanisms of our present social and political systems. To fight pollution and preserve our environment is a fine and worthy cause, but lacking a wider perspective of knowledge and method it can only remove a few superficial symptoms of a disease, but hazily diagnosed and of origin unknown. The time is past when we have to deal with simple problems and hope for individual solutions. The size and complexity of society is now such that changing a few variables as a consequence of a ponderous, ignorant and unrepresentative political process, is likely, through a readjustment of the internal forces of the system, to produce unexpected results in quite other parts of the system, which will not easily be seen as resulting from the new policy.

Present structures of government and of learning are not geared to the new necessities. Government agencies are normally static, vertical structures, designed for the needs of earlier, simpler days. In most countries, for example, it is not possible to envisage and act on the urban situation in its totality; responsibility is disseminated over a dozen specialized departments and agencies, each preoccupied with a single element. Together with such structural inadequacy, conceptual thinking for the future is still mainly of a linear projection type, quite unsuitable for a high inertia dynamic situation. Where in government is it possible to link and measure the cross impact—say of the world monetary situation, world population increase, environmental deterioration, student unrest and the deepening alienation of city dwellers?

The growth of knowledge is similarly constrained within an equally rigid pattern of disciplines, appropriate enough a century ago. The significant advances in the natural sciences are, however, no longer in the classical categories such as chemistry, physics or geology. The interface subjects such as biochemistry, geophysics, molecular biology, cybernetics or neuro-physiology have, through the vitality of their proponents and the evident importance of their discoveries, been accommodated, at least in the United States, within the traditional university structures, although old Europe still clings, in the main, to its outworn faculty system. Yet at the frontiers, knowledge is developing its own dynamics. The primary interface subjects are forging new relationships with one another producing new topics of possibly ephemeral, although of great immediate, importance—temporary sciences, as it were, at points of concentration and cross impact of different significant discoveries. Science then, is itself becoming a kaleidoscopic, kinetic evolutionary activity for which present attitudes and structures are archaic. This dynamic development does not stop at the frontiers of natural science; it pervades the social sciences and will influence the humanities producing that unity of knowledge which was *science* before the Anglo-Saxon heresy construed the term narrowly in terms of natural philosophy.

While many statesmen and thinkers are aware of these matters in some real detail and are deeply concerned with the gravity and complexity of the problems now facing man, the inertia of the machine, the static nature of political thinking and the genius of the establishment for self-perpetuation makes it difficult for them to break out of the present impasse. It was Max Planck who said that a new principle never finds easy acceptance from traditional thinkers; it requires the passage of time and the arising of a new generation, unbound by the old theories, to accept the new.

In face of this difficulty a small international group of scientists, industrialists, and bankers, without direct responsibility within national administrations but collectively possessing a good deal of influence have formed a loose organization which they named the "Club of Rome," so called because it was in the oldest of all the academies, the *Academia dei Lincei* of Rome, that they held their first meeting. These men, who are united in their conviction of the gravity of the situation now facing mankind, have no possible vested interest in perpetuating the old inadequate thinking and structures and no ambitions of power toward the new. They are ready to disband as soon as their main objectives have been achieved.

The first goal of the Club of Rome is to alert those in the highest political positions as to the nature, complexity and gravity of the problems which confront them and of the need to accept new concepts and approaches. An inner group of the Club has already visited Washington and Moscow for such discussions; they have talked with the Prime Minister and senior officials in Canada, in Tokyo and elsewhere. The governments of Austria and Switzerland have invited the group to visit their capitols to debate with ministers and other authorities as to the situation. This apolitical action on politicians will continue.

The second objective of the Club of Rome is essentially methodological, to work out a method of describing the various elements of the problem of contemporary society, to determine the nature and significance of the cross impacts and to build a first and necessarily crude first dynamic model of world problems. Before devising such a model, a great deal of consultation is necessary with the few scholars who have already taken steps in this direction. This is now being done, and the project, entitled "The Predicament of Mankind" will, it is hoped, be launched this year with international financing. Expectations are that it will be carried out by a team of Western Europeans, Americans, Russians and Japanese. A preliminary simulation model has already been initiated under Professor Jay Forrester at Massachusetts Institute of Technology.

The Rome Club approach is extremely ambitious, but at the same time being accomplished in a quiet and modest manner. It is either extremely naive or extremely sophisticated.

The Predicament of Mankind

The final question to be raised is how grave in fact is the situation? Does it differ in quality from previous situations to an extent that creates a real crisis to the human race or is it just the accumulation of the problems of society, aggravated by the industrial revolution and technology, but essentially those of man from his beginnings?

To my mind the problematique is one of major crisis for the race—a crisis which despite its sociological and other manifestations may be inherently biological. The question we cannot yet answer is, can men generally learn to live with affluence or will prosperity suffocate, poison and enfeeble the species? We know that many species of animals degenerate rapidly in the absence of predators, but we assume that man—understanding albeit dimly his own functioning, yet imagining a destiny for his race—can overcome this.

This may well prove to be true and indeed must be made so. For the first time in human history large numbers of people are free from the immediate obligation of finding food and shelter and protecting their families from enemies. At the same time there is a general loss of faith in religion, while rising prosperity has blunted the appetite of the social reformer; the credibility of party politics is rapidly vanishing. What then are the incentives for men, near-saturated with consumption goods, to work, to drive forward or even to continue living? Is his future to be one of leisure, boredom and satiety in mass surroundings, or will this inevitably lead to race degeneration, speeded up by the welfare state's success in securing the survival of the feeble and the unfit? Certainly the process of organic evolution which produced man is no longer relevant to his future. Its time scale of mutation trial and error is impossibly long for operation on a creature semi-conscious of his own situation and apparently hell bent on self-destruction. We need a wholly new path of evolution for this imperfect but self-criticizing organism.

Throughout the ages people and especially the young have questioned the meaning and aim of existence, have experienced the desire of man to be more than man, but in the main they have had to be satisfied with the answers of the traditional religions and made to forget the ultimate destiny in the struggle for existence. This is no longer so; the young seek still but will no longer be fobbed off by the glib answer and supernational constraint, nor will they be happy with bread and circuses. The drug cult, triggered off in its present phase, is one symptom of the search for new perceptions—mainly, alas, simply abused. The mushrooming of new religions and philosophies, mainly oriental in origin and mainly transparently insufficient, is another sign of the search for a higher level of consciousness, with many precedents from Meister Eckhart to the 12th century Sufi poets, explored with infinitely greater wisdom and subtlety.

In the meanwhile, lacking this new evolutionary path, what shall we do? We must try to know a little more about ourselves and our functioning, learn to manage our complex systems better and introduce an emergency of conservation until we are ready to act. We need a new ethic whose first criterion in deciding between alternatives is whether or not the result will heighten or lower man's capacity to survive.

Alexander King was born in Scotland and educated at the Imperial College of Science, London, and the University of Munich. He taught and did research in physical chemistry in London. During the war he was Deputy Science Adviser to the Minister of Production, and later head of the British Commonwealth Scientific Office in Washington, D.C. Later he became head of the scientific secretariat of the British cabinet and scientific adviser to the Lord President of the Council. During this period he was chairman of the governing board of the European Productivity Agency, and later its director. He is now the Director General for Scientific Affairs at the Organization for Economic Cooperation and Development (OECD) in Paris. Dr. King's publications include various chemistry textbooks, and his papers have been published in many scientific journals—such as the *Journal of the Chemical Society* and the *Faraday Society*. Dr. King is an Associate of the Center for the Study of Democratic Institutions.

ABOUT THE EDITORS. . .

CLIFTON FADIMAN, editorial consultant to The Center for the Study of Democratic Institutions, has a long-established reputation as essayist, critic, anthologist, encyclopedist, and radio and television personality. He was for many years book critic for *The New Yorker*. He continues to serve as one of the judges of the Book-of-the-Month club. His published works range from literature (The Lifetime Reading Plan) to mathematics (*Fantasia Mathematica* and *The Mathematical Magpie*.) He is a member of the board of editors of *Encyclopaedia Britannica* and, as author of the article on Children's Literature, a contributor to the set. He is presently at work on an extensive critical history of children's literature.

JEAN DUNCAN WHITE was born in California and educated at Florida State University, the University of Minnesota and Stanford University; and she has been a member of the Taliesin Fellowship at the Frank Lloyd Wright Foundation in Spring Green, Wisconsin. From 1953 to 1956 she was director of the office of the Committee on Public Exercises at Stanford University; later, she was employed in the aerospace industries as a technical editor. Since 1969 she has been on the editorial staff of The Center for the Study of Democratic Institutions, Santa Barbara, as an editor.

Composition by: Space Graphics, Inc., Palo Alto, Ca.